MEGO

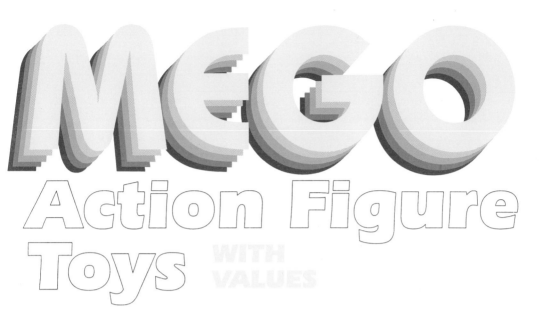

MEGO
Action Figure
Toys
WITH VALUES

John Bonavita

Schiffer Publishing Ltd

77 Lower Valley Road, Atglen, PA 19310

To my Darling Wife Diana

Without her support and verbal encouragement
this book would not have been possible.

Copyright © 1996 by John Bonavita

Printed in China

ISBN: 0-7643-0025-3

Book Design by Audrey L. Whiteside

**Library of Congress Cataloging-in-
Publication Data**

Bonavita, John
    Mego action figure toys/John
Bonavita.
        p.   cm.
    Includes index.
    ISBN 0-7643-0025-3
    1. Action figures (Toys)--Collectors
and collecting--Catalogs. 2. Mego Cor-
poration--Catalogs. 1. Title.
MK4894.2.M44A4   1996
688.7'28'0973--dc20   96-9353
                              CIP

Published by Schiffer Publishing, Ltd.
77 Lower Valley Road
Atglen, PA 19310
Phone: (610) 593-1777
Fax: (610) 593-2002
Please write for a free catalog.
This book may be purchased from the publisher.
Please include $2.95 for shipping.
Try your bookstore first.

Contents

Acknowledgments

I would like to thank the following people who over the past fifteen years have made this book possible with their knowledge, joy of collecting, and support:

My Mother and Father, Maria Bluni, Joe Montore, Peter Gumbrecht, Guy Redwing, Dave Stevenson, Cristiano Rucco, Mark Bonavita, Dave Jakubowski, John McGonagle, Gary Maguire, Hiroki Sakata, Linda Young.

Special Thanks to Mr. Schiffer and the staff of Schiffer Publishing for making this dream a reality.

Foreword

Most children who grew up in America during the 1970s have owned or played with at least one Mego action figure during their lifetime. The company's male-orientated action figure categories were so popular that for years they easily dominated their field with very little competition. Children instantly took to Mego's human-like figures and spent many hours creating imaginary adventures with them. Parents loved the idea of a toy that not only proved fun to play with but was mentally stimulating as well.

Today Mego action figures and accessories are fondly remembered by both non-collectors and collectors alike. While often described as simplistic, primitive, and naive compared to today's slick high-tech action figures, it is these very qualities that have made collecting Mego action figures and accessories a rapidly growing segment of the toy collectors' community. Mego delighted and enchanted a whole generation of children with their high standard of quality and authentic attention to detail. It is these same children, now adults, who are once again rediscovering their old toy friends and reliving many childhood memories of playing with Mego toys.

Introduction

This book is a collector's guide to the hundreds of action figures, playsets, and play toys manufactured by Mego from 1970 through 1982. Because new discoveries are still being made on a regular basis worldwide, it is not, however, the definitive guide. With no archive or master production list of its products available, Mego has been a mystery to collectors who have wondered at what exactly the toy company manufactured. With the majority of its toys based upon licensed properties, Mego was often forced to abandon or develop new products on short notice. Former employees have regularly stated that the media driven company moved so quickly that even they had a difficult time keeping track of what was actually manufactured. While this limitation may make a definitive guide impossible, this book contains virtually all of the company's known work. As an added feature, a Mego history and price guide is included, as well as a detailed listing of the company's known foreign action figure releases.

How to Use This Book

How This Book Has Been Organized

The action figure product lines produced by Mego between 1970 and 1982 have been organized by grouping for easy reference. They are as follows:

Original Action Figures
Non licensed and original action figure characters created by Mego.

TV Action Figures and Personalities
Licensed action figures that are based on television programs and personalities.

Movie Action Figures
Licensed action figures that are based on theatrical movies.

Super Hero Action Figures
Marvel and DC Super Heroes.

The contents of each chapter have been organized in the alphabetical order by the action figure line's full product name. Each product name will be followed by the dates of its availability: for example, *Wizard of Oz* (1974-76). Action figures that were later reissued will also feature reissue dates: example *Mad Monster Series* (1974-75), (1980).

The Collector Notes section found at the beginning of each product listing will feature pertinent information for collectors on the subject action figure line.

Values

Values are based upon years of collecting, communication with collectors world-wide, and current market prices observed at toy shows and through collectible publications. They are the prices that collectors can reasonably expect to pay at shows or through mail order. As always, prices are relative, and ultimately a item is worth the price of its demand and what a buyer is willing to pay.

Note: If you have toys to sell and you sell them to a dealer who is planning on reselling them, you will *not* obtain the prices reported in this book. You should expect to achieve about fifty percent of these prices. In order for your items to be of interest to a buyer who plans to resell them, they must be purchased for considerably less than the prices listed here.

Condition

For each item listed, the following two value and condition categories strictly exist: Mint and MIB. These are defined as follows:

Mint
Item is complete with all accessories. Item is in pristine condition, unplayed with, and like new. A playset or play toy item has all of its stickers, even if applied to the toy.

MIB
Item possesses all of the attributes of Mint but with the addition of being carded or boxed in its original display packaging which is like new. Box may be opened. Bubble cards that have been partially removed from cards or bubbles that have been slit so that figure can be removed are not considered MIB.

Less then Mint or MIB
Items in less then MIB or Mint condition would be devalued according to its condition. Features to consider are package condition, price tag placement, tears, missing accessories, and general toy (played with) condition.

Special Terms Explained

If a value is not given for a particular item the following will be present in their place: NSR, UKN, NP or NA. These are defined as follows:

NSR (No Sales Recorded): Item is known to have been available but is so rare that an accurate value can not be attributed to it. When purchasing these items it is solely up to the seller and buyer as to what it value is.

UKN (Unknown): It is unknown if this item was mass produced for consumer retail sales. Prototypes are known to exist.

NP (Never Produced): It is known with a degree of certainty that this item was not produced for retail sale. Prototypes may possibly exit.

NA (Not Available). Item was not available for retail sale individually or in this format.

Identifying a Mego Toy

Packaged Mego action figures, playsets, and play toys issued in the US will feature the company's name somewhere on the package as well as on the actual toy. Loose, out of package action figures are generally marked Mego on their back between their shoulder blades along with the company's patent information. The back of each action figure's head may also be marked Mego or in rare examples feature no mark at all. If a licensed property, heads will be marked with owner's trade mark and copyright date: for example, © DC Comics 1977.

Mego products distributed or manufactured exclusively for foreign retail sales usually feature the word Mego (along with that of their foreign distributor) on them for identification.

Action Figure Packaging

Before 1974, the majority of Mego action figures were available in solid boxes that did not allow for the viewing of the enclosed action figure. A full color drawing of the character, along with its name, adorn the front and back of the box for customer identification. At the insistence of retailers, Mego modified its solid action figure package with a clear plastic window to allow for contents viewing. This had the positive effect of increasing sales as well as eliminating damage caused to the figure and package by in-store opening of boxes by children and parents.

In 1974 Mego refined a protective clear blister pack which it had used sparingly two years earlier. This type of package would hold a figure securely to a cardboard card for easy peg display. Action figures could now be completely viewed by customers and at the same time be protected against pilfering and handling. Mego offered retailers the option of ordering figures in either this new blister pack or older window box styles. By 1976 the company switched entirely to bubble card packaging.

Caring for Action Figures

All Mego action figures (including those manufactured by other companies) are made from an organic compound called plastic. Soft plastic, otherwise known as vinyl, is easy to mold and commonly used for the manufacturing of detailed heads. Harder, less pliable plastics are normally used for bodies, arms, legs, and for action figure accessories. As an organic compound, all plastics are susceptible to element exposure and especially to that of ultraviolet light. When exposed to ultraviolet light, which is found in sunlight, plastic begins to undergo a chemical reaction or breakdown. As a result accessories may melt, vinyl heads may become faded or discolored, and bodies may become brittle— resulting in cracks as well as broken leg and arm joints.

While the majority of action figures should last a lifetime with very little outward signs of the plastic damage just described, collectors can help insure the condition of their collections by storing and displaying figures in a cool, dry place away from direct sunlight, heat, and dampness. Action figures should also not be overly handled or played with as this may result in body and joint cracking. If possible, figures should be stored in boxes (acid free boxes are of a higher quality then common boxes and preferred for loose figures) which will limit their exposure to the elements.

Finding Mego Action Figures

Mego action figures and accessories can be found at a variety of outlets. The company's products were so prolific that collectors should have no problem finding examples at local toy shows, collectible stores, flea markets, garage sales, and specialty shops. Many action figure related publications routinely feature articles on Mego toys and are readily available to collectors through book stores and comic shops.

Action figure collector clubs are also a prime source of Mego information and can prove invaluable in creating contacts with fellow Mego collectors worldwide. One of the first and largest, The Classic Action Figure Collectors Club, continuously publishes information on Mego and its history in its official club magazine, Collect 'Em All. With over one thousand members worldwide, it boast hundreds of collectors whose major interest is Mego. (For more information write to C.A.C.C., P.O. Box 2095, Halesite, New York 11743.)

A New Discovery

If you have discovered a previously unknown Mego item, or if you have an action figure, playset, or play toy that is missing from the listings in this book, please contact the author immediately. Collectors worldwide will be indebted to you as it is only through the sharing of information and knowledge that our collectors' community will grow. Acknowledgment and credit for new discoveries or unlisted items will be given in future updates to this book.

Chapter One
The History of Mego

A Giant Leap Forward

Founded by Mr. David Abrams in the early 1950s, Mego was best known as an importer of inexpensive rack toys and holiday novelties. While largely unknown to the general public, Mego found success with under-a-dollar products that could be found in five and dime stores across America, as well as around the world. Most of these generic items were distributed without a copyright date or company trademark and were simply identified as being made in Hong Kong. The company's giant leap forward from relative obscurity into the annuals of collector history would not come until 1971. It was during that year that Mego would begin its ascent and earn praise as being what collectors now commonly refer to as *The World's Greatest Action Figure Company*.

Before 1971, Mego was best known for its inexpensive novelties and toys.

In 1971, Martin B. Abrams was promoted to president of Mego. A recent marketing graduate from New York University, the then twenty-eight-year old Abrams had the bright idea of paying top dollar royalties for the exclusive rights to use the image of popular movie, comic book, and TV characters. While licensing had been part of the toy industry since its inception, it was viewed as perilous, fraught with expensive failures, and dependent upon a fickle public. Due to these limitations, licensing during this period accounted for a small percentage of the overall industry and was usually reserved for well-known characters. Undaunted by the risk involved and tired of producing copies of popular action figures and fashion dolls of the period, Abrams quickly guided Mego into the world of licensing by acquiring virtually every major hot property of the time with the sole intent of producing action figures. With a keen sense of what would and would not sell, the energetic Abrams would often spend his free time frequenting toy stores and asking children questions as to who their favorite heroes and TV stars were. Armed with this knowledge, the young company president would propel Mego from the ranking of three hundred in 1970 to number six out of all toy companies by the end of the decade.

A Formula For Success

Martin Abrams once referred to the toy industry as part show biz. He realized at an early stage that if a particular action figure line was not popular with toy buyers (those who represented the nation's retail stores), it would never have a chance at reaching children. The young showman wooed buyers and obtained large purchase orders by staging some of the most memorable and exciting action figure introductions in Toy Fair history. (Toy Fair is the industry's equivalent of a trade show where new toys are offered and sold to the nation's retailers. It is an annual event held in New York during the month of February). While other companies frowned and scoffed at the upstart company and its unorthodox president, Abrams saw Mego's success grow with no end in sight.

One of Mego and Abrams' most notable introductions in turn became a media grabbing coup. To show off the company's new 1975 *Wizard of Oz* action figure and playset line, Abrams hosted a party at the famed Grand Ballroom of New York's Waldorf-Astoria Hotel. Inviting over one thousand of the retail industry's most influential people, the company introduced every surviving star of the MGM classic including *Tin Man* Jack Haley and *Scarecrow* Ray Bolger. With buyers delighted with the new figure toy line and occupied with seeking autographs, Mego saw its *Wizard of Oz* orders grow, making it an instant hit. While the party cost Mego the substantial sum of $50,000 to stage, it and other star-studded introductions in the year to come left a lasting impression on the media, toy buyers, and consumers. Mego had left its rack toy image behind and had become a major toy manufacturer.

Interchangeable Body

With the goal of minimizing the company's exposure to a license failure, Abrams and Mego's toy designers came up with a novel approach to producing action figures. Rather than molding each specific character into action figure form, which would be costly, the company patented a soft plastic 8" fully interchangeable jointed body that could easily change into an infinite number of characters. If a figure failed, Mego simply and quickly could convert it into another by changing its head and outfit. This new

14

Celebrity studded 1976 press introduction of
the Muhammad Ali 9" action figure.

8" body also had the added benefit of costing less to produce then the then industry standard 12" action figure body made popular by Hasbro's *GI Joe*. It would also offer consumers more play value then a 12" action figure as it was better suited for playsets and accessories.

In 1974, Mego's 8" action figure formula proved a rewarding success. Acquiring the figure rights to the highly touted *Planet of the Apes* television series, which was based upon the popular movies of the same name, Mego had five of the show's major characters in mass production for the all important upcoming holiday season. What was thought to be a ratings and licensing winner proved to be a failure. After the show's fall premier, ratings declined drastically and the expensive series was quickly canceled. Mego, faced with thousands of unwanted figures, simply converted unshipped inventory into other characters—diverting what could otherwise have been a crippling financial blow. This ground-breaking approach to figure production was an example of Mego's innovation which would become a company's hallmark throughout the 1970s.

Family Business

While many collectors acknowledge the genius of Martin Abrams in helping to create *The World's Greatest Action Figure Company*, Mego was truly a family business with all involved responsible for its success. In a period of time when most large American businesses were transforming from family enterprises into corporate, board member run entities, Mego remained firmly entrenched in family. Martin Abrams presided as president and the main creative force of the company in New York. His father and company founder, David Abrams, oversaw all of Mego's manufacturing in Hong Kong. Madeline Abrams, David's mother and co-designer of many of the company's action figure outfits, oversaw the manufacturing and quality of all costumes which at times totaled over 12 million in annual production. Martin's younger brother Howard, who is credited with coining the name Mego by saying "me go too" as a child every time his father traveled, aided his brother by helping with the company's daily operations.

The Roaring 1970s

Each year with Martin Abrams' guidance as president of Mego saw the company's success and profits grow. With a string of well picked hits and the ability to quickly bring "hot" licensed products to market, Mego quickly became the dominant maker of action figures in America. Even Hasbro, manufacturer of the nation's most popular action figure, bowed to the company's success by scaling its *GI Joe* down to the new Mego created action figure standard of 8" in 1976.

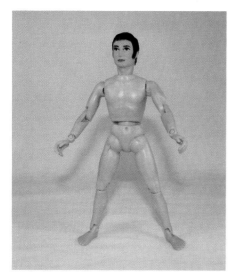

Mego's revolutionary 8" action figure body.

With its interchangeable head, the basic Mego action figure body could assume any identity.

Under the guidance of the ever energetic president Mego looked beyond the success of its action figure accomplishments and diversified into other areas of toy production. A slew of new non-action figure related products were developed and offered to retailers. These items ranged from board games, such as the successful *Othello* and crudely named *Ballbusters*, to the best selling talking educational Robot, *2XL*. With various degrees of success Mego would also offer retailers electronic hand-held video games, child cosmetics, miniature vehicles, construction sets, stuffed animals, science kits, costume jewelry, educational toys, baby dolls, infant toys, car racing sets, bicycle accessories, and preschool toys.

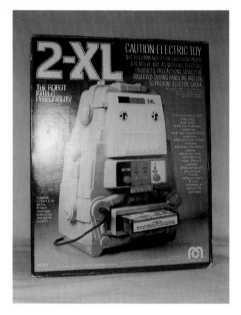

The popular *2XL* educational toy disguised as a talking Robot.

One of the many different products introduced during the late 1970s.

The Company Overseas

While limited due to the diverse tastes of European, Asian, South American, and African consumers, Mego maintained offices and established distribution agents overseas through its subsidiaries. Many of the company's more popular US action figure lines were widely available and sold throughout Europe, with Britain and Italy being its greatest importer. Distributed and in some cases licensed by European toy companies, many of these figures feature completely different packaging and artwork from their American counterparts.

Mego also produced foreign action figure exclusives, usually at the request of its foreign customers. These were usually based upon comic, TV, and movie personalities popular to a particular country. These exclusive action figures feature some of the company's best sculpturing and costume work. Difficult to find, many remain unknown and a mystery to collectors today.

1975 Italian Mego magazine advertisement featuring *Action Jackson* and the Italian exclusive *Tex Willer*.

Super Heroes

Perhaps Martin Abrams' greatest achievement and Mego's greatest legacy to collectors is its *Official World's Greatest Super Heroes* 8" line of action figures. Acquiring the license rights from both Marvel and DC Comics in 1971, Mego's 8" line of Super Heroes grew from an initial offering of four figures in 1972 to a roster of over thirty characters by 1977. Figures such as *Superman, Batman, Capt. America*, and *Spiderman* proved so popular and long-lived that pioneering techniques such as the use of a clear blister pack for figure protection and eye catching artwork by real comic book artists can be attributed to them.

Mego kept their Super Hero line fresh by offering new figures on a annual basis and intentionally made select figures hard to find by rotating characters in and out of store delivery assortments. Not only did this keep children interested in obtaining new figures, it often garnered repeat visits to toy stores by parents. This practice, now common to toy makers today, often led to additional sales as parents would often buy another character for a child rather than leaving empty handed. The company also produced villains and female characters, which until recently were not deemed financially viable by toy manufacturers because of the belief that most children prefer male heroes as opposed to female heroines or villans of either gender.

Super Heroes became a staple product, often leading all of Mego's other action figure categories in sales. With figures ranging from 3 3/4" to 22" in size, Super Heroes would remain in continuous production until 1982.

After their quick success, Mego immediately
announced new Super Hero action figures.

Early *Planet of the Apes* magazine advertisement.

Mego on Television

With most of its licensed products based upon syndicated and prime time TV programs, television was a natural promotional choice for Mego. During the 1970s the company invested millions of dollars into television advertising, which until that point was unheard of for a toy company. While the company still advertised in traditional print mediums such as comic books and magazines, much of its rapid success can be attributed to its unique television commercials which aired during the mid to late 1970s.

Television advertising of Mego products was primarily used during the holidays as well as during peak weekday and weekend children viewing hours. Mego commercials utilized novel techniques that were more akin to Hollywood movies then to rival toy commercials of the period. The commercials were filled with distinct character voices, suggestive open-ended plots (that a child could resolve at home with his or her own action figure), and fast comic book paced action. These commercials also had the added benefit of featuring authentic film footage, theme music, and special effects from their licensed namesakes. These "mini movies" were like nothing children had been exposed to before and became an instant hit.

Today, with a VCR in almost every home, Mego commercials are avidly sought, traded, and collected. Widely available through action figure collector clubs as well as at toy shows and conventions, Mego commercials remain as fresh and enjoyable when viewed today as they once did when first aired.

A Costly Mistake

In 1977 a science fiction film named *Star Wars* was offered to Mego for consideration as a possible action figure toy line. The 20th Century Fox produced film was the brain child of a little known director named George Lucas, who found success years earlier with a film called *American Graffiti*. *Star Wars*, which featured a largely unknown cast, concerned the battle between an evil space empire and a band of rebels. In a decision that would prove disastrous, Mego passed up on the rights to produce *Star Wars* figures and accessories. Not since *Planet of the Apes* had there been a popular science fiction film, and the genre was considered dead. It was perhaps due to this assumption—that movie audiences would not be interested in what appeared to be a "space opera"—that caused a lack of interest on the part of Mego. *Star Wars* was eventually licensed by Kenner Toys. When it exploded across movie screens around the world on May 31, 1977, it would forever change the perception of science fiction and the world of action figures.

1980 Mego television commercial schedule.

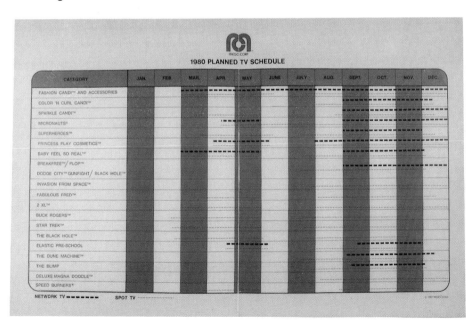

The Next Blockbuster

The massive popularity of *Star Wars* caused a unparalleled effect that caught retailers and Hollywood by surprise. Becoming the highest grossing movie of all time, the movie was responsible for over a billion dollars in retail sales of clothing, books, video games, and toys. *Star Wars* redefined the term "blockbuster" and invigorated a whole genre. Hollywood, hoping to cash in on the public's new found appetite for science fiction, green lighted a host of films and TV series that featured record breaking budgets and built-in mass merchandise appeal. Mego, whose action figure dominance was eroded by the popularity of Kenner's best selling 3 3/4" *Star Wars* figures, responded by acquiring the figure rights to the majority of these aspiring late 1970s projects.

Mego paid premium fees for the right to produce action figures, playsets, and play toys based upon Paramount Pictures: *Star Trek: The Motion Picture*, Walt Disney: *The Black Hole*, United Artists: *Moon Raker*, and Universal's movie and spin-off television series *Buck Rogers in the 25th Century*. The toy company hoped that at least one would be a *Star Wars* magnitude hit helping to usher the company well into the 1980s.

To the dismay of Mego and the studios involved, each science fiction film licensed by the toy company proved merchandising failures. With its movie action figures and playsets languishing on retail shelves, Mego's long running string of action figure hits established in the early 1970s was at an end.

Bankruptcy

Saddled with the expense of its movie failures, Mego entered the new decade in disarray. With unrelated internal pressures mounting within the company and a lack of new products to help offset its action figure failures, Mego's market share plummeted. Between 1980 and 1983 the company was forced to sell much of its US and foreign assets as well as curtail its overall operations to stay in business. With layoffs (from a high of over 2,000 employees during the late 1970s to less then 30 by 1983) and mounting debt, the company's troubles were widely publicized in the nation's financial newspapers.

Critics pointed out many of Mego's blunders, including its over reliance on licensing, lack of original ideas (which many noted had been a company hallmark in the past), and a slow approach at taking advantage of fads such as video games. When the company did produce a line of hand held video games they were simply outclassed by their competitors. Even the company's prized DC and Marvel Comic Super Hero product licenses, which were once responsible for steady retail sales, were weakened by neglect and a lack of new products.

By June of 1982, Mego was overwhelmed by more than $50 million in debt and was forced into filing for Chapter 11 bankruptcy protection (a proceeding of which it emerged a year later but not as a maker of toys). The company who had dominated the entire action figure market during the 1970s and pioneered much of what is now common place closed its doors forever. *The World's Greatest Action Figure Company* had come to a end.

Chapter Two
Questions, Answers, and Mysteries

The following are the most common questions asked by collectors concerning Mego. Answers have been based on research of Mego documents, interviews with former company employees, and correspondence with fellow action figure collectors.

What is a *Kresge* style card?

In 1973 Mego developed a blister pack that was the forerunner of what collectors now commonly refer to as the "Mego bubble card." Kresge was a general merchandise department store (today known as K Mart) which demanded that Mego's action figures be compatible with its merchandise "peg display" system. Mego did so, and due to the department stores large action figure orders, printed the name "Kresge" on each package.

Collectors refer to any Mego blister pack that feature the bubble down the middle rather then to one side as a Kresge card. This style of blister packs may or may not have the word Kresge printed on it.

Kresge style blister cards feature a clear plastic bubble down the middle of the card rather than to one side.

Mego and Lion Rock

American collectors have often been puzzled by the Mego 6" action figure body used for the company's *Teen Titan* action figures (as well as Mego's *WWII Heroes*). Marked Lion Rock (instead of Mego) these figure bodies were originally manufactured for foreign sales. Lion Rock was a subsidiary of Mego that designed, created, and in part manufactured its own toy lines for foreign markets. While the name Lion Rock has been found exclusively for identification of the company's 6" action figure body, other sized foreign Mego figures have also been found marked Lion Rock.

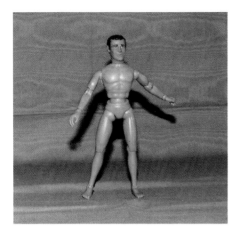

Mego 6" action figure body which is marked Lion Rock.

1975 Super Hero mini consumer action figure catalog.

Mini Catalogs

To keep children informed of its various action figure lines, Mego included a mini product catalog with the majority of its playsets during the mid 1970s. Used sparingly by past toy manufacturers, Mego disguised its mini catalogs as exciting accessories by printing their inclusion on the playset package. This practice proved a success as children would check off the figures they had and implored parents to purchase the ones they needed. Printed in full color, each catalog opened to include photographs of various action figure lines available for that particular year. Catalogs were also issued in foreign countries and are highly desired by US Mego collectors as they often pictured exclusive foreign offerings. Due to their fragile and disposable nature, most catalogs, both US and foreign, are hard to find today and command high prices by dealers.

What is a Dealer Product Catalog?

Dealer product catalogs are catalogs that were not meant for the general public but rather were issued to the nation's retailers for solicitation. Featuring slick paper and graphics, these full size catalogs were printed in limited amounts and given out to prospective customers during industry trade shows. Inside would be the company's proposed new toy lines for the upcoming year (usually prototypes and mockups) as well as returning favorites. Retailers chose products that interested them and placed a order. Toys that experienced very few retail orders were either canceled or solicited again at a latter date. If a particular toy was mainly chosen by a major retail account it was usually produced in limited quantities as a store exclusive.

Desired by advanced collectors, dealer product catalogs are often the only source of information concerning hard to find or never produced toys. This, coupled with their disposable nature by retailers once used, make them extremely difficult to acquire. Foreign distributor catalogs that feature Mego products are virtually impossible to find in the US. Collectors should expect to pay a premium for any US or foreign Mego dealer product catalog offered them.

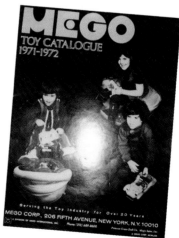

Mego 1971-1972 Dealer Product Catalog.

Store Displays and Promotions

In 1972, Mego included in most 8" action figure retail orders a free cardboard counter box display stand. Designed for the company's box type of action figure packaging, each counter box could be set up within seconds and offered retailers an easy solution for action figure display. Each display box featured a full color action drawing of each character (lifted from the actual action figure package) available to that particular assortment. After the figures were sold, most boxes were thrown out, explaining their scarcity today. With the company switching entirely to bubble card packaging for its action figures late in 1976, the practice of including a counter display was discontinued in favor of peg display.

Mego offered very few retail promotional offers during its action figure history. One exciting promotion that did occurr involved the company's Super Heroes and took place in 1980. Titled *"A Super Heroes Shopping Spree Sweepstakes"* it was open to anyone, purchase not required. With a total of four winners, each would be able to load as many Mego products into a shopping cart as possible and take them home for free. During the sweepstakes, and as a bonus incentive to paying customers, Mego gave out a free Marvel or DC poster with every Super Hero action figure purchased. Each poster measured 16" X 20" and featured either DC or Marvel Super Heroes battling prehistoric monsters running amuck.

8" World's Greatest Super Hero 8" action figure store display.

26

Announcement for the 1980 *Super Heroes
Shopping Spree Sweepstakes*.

Never Produced Figures

During the successful days of the mid 1970s Mego considered or acquired the rights to a host of promising properties ranging from motion picture and TV programs to comic book and literary heroes. While only a small percentage were actually produced into action figure lines, most were not and were subsequently forgotten. Collectors can now only imagine what Mego action figures based on pulp heroes such as *Doc Savage, The Green Hornet, The Phantom,* and TV series such as *Kung Fu, Land of the Lost, The Invisible Man, Joanie Loves Chachi, The Fall Guy,* and *Hill Street Blues* would have looked like. Most of these Mego acquired licenses never made it as far as the prototype stage and those that did, such as TV's *Dallas* and the movie *Grease,* offer tantalizing glimpses at what possibly could have been.

Never produced figures were also subject to figure lines that were in production. As a matter of toy industry practice, the majority of best selling action figure lines were expanded with new character editions each year. This practice often breathed new interest into an older action figure line which hopefully would extend its retail

27

life. Mego was no exception to this practice and regularly expanded many of its more popular figure lines with new characters when retail demand warranted it. Additions to the popular *Star Trek, Super Heroes, Dukes of Hazards*, and *Buck Rogers* are known to have been planned, but whether due to weak projected sales or lack of interest on the part of retailers, they did not materialize. While prototypes may exist for many of these planned characters, no authentic examples have been found. It is believed that like many licensed properties considered for production, many of these characters existed only on paper subject to the interest of retailers.

Artwork from the proposed, but never produced, *Doc Savage* action figure line.

Almost Official

During the late 1970s Mego stopped offering retailers many of the playsets and accessories designed for its 8" Super Hero. While Mego chose to concentrate on its movie based offerings, companies such as Empire and Tara Toys offered retailers Super Hero accessories that were licensed but not sanctioned by Mego: Empire produced generic Super Hero vehicles while Tara manufactured a unique playset named the Hulk Hide Away. Manufactured specifically as a accessory for Mego's 8" Hulk action figure, it was sold only through the Sears Christmas catalog in 1979 and 1980. The playset featured a Mego type transformation chamber as well as a cardboard figure of the never produced Dr. Bruce Banner character.

Advertisement for Tara Toys' Hulk Hide Away
playset and Empire's Hulk Van.

US Mystery Figures

Mego produced hundreds of action figures over a twelve year period, many of which were available only in certain regions or as exclusives. This fact combined with the small amount of information available to collectors over past years has contributed to the many sightings of mysterious or unknown Mego figures. With action figure collecting growing in popularity and the proliferation of reference books, publications, and collectors clubs making information more readily available, most Mego mysteries that have occupied collectors over the past twenty years have been solved or dismissed.

One of the most popular of all Mego mysteries involves the television show *Logan's Run*. In 1977, Mego acquired the action figure rights to a new science fiction television program called *Logan's Run*. Based upon the hit movie of the same name, the property's outlandish setting and characters were perfect for an action figure line. It is believed that 8" figures based upon the lead characters of Logan, Jessica, and Rem were produced in small amounts awaiting US distribution. When the show was quickly canceled, Mego ceased further figure manufacturing and was rumored to have destroyed its existing *Logan's Run* inventory. To date, no authentic Logan's Run action figures have been found by collectors.

A small quantity of these mysterious 8" Mego action figures in blue flight suits with yellow helmets were discovered during the early 1980s.

Foreign Mystery Figures

With the advent of inexpensive communications, more and more US collectors are communicating with their overseas foreign counterparts. As a result, many foreign Mego discoveries have been made but just as many mysteries have been uncovered. European rumors and sightings of action figures based upon the mid 1970s series of *Three Musketeer* films as well as the 1980 *Flash Gordon* movie have spread rapidly amongst US collectors. Foreign collectors have also spoken of action figures ranging from the UK comic book hero *Dan Dare* to Australian *Robin Hood* character additions of *Maid Marion* and the *Sheriff of Nottingham*.

The 1983 Toy Line

As part of Mego's restructuring, many of its licenses, patents, and proposed toy lines were sold to rival companies to satisfy creditors. One such action figure line believed to have been part of this liquidation action was purchased and distributed by Multi Toy Corp. in 1983. Based upon the Mexican pop group *Menudo* these figures utilized Mego's 8" action figure body as well as its district clothing and head molding style. Though partially "rubbed out" from its body mold during manufacturing, the word Mego can still be seen between each figure's back shoulder blades on early figures.

8" *Menudo* action figure issued by Multi Toy Corp. in 1983.

Pac and Phoenix Toys

With Mego's manufacturing facilities in Hong Kong liquidated, the company in 1982 entered into an agreement with a Long Island, New York, based toy maker named Pac Corp. Pac would produce Mego's upcoming 1983 toy line with the understanding that if the troubled toy maker could not make its scheduled payments to them, they would become sole owner of the proposed product line. In 1983, this scenario occurred when Mego could not satisfy existing creditors nor secure new financing. Mego was now officially out of the toy business and Pac, now renamed Phoenix Toys, was left with the once mighty toy company's proposed 1983 toy line.

In 1983, Phoenix Toys (it is believed that former Mego employees were retained by Pac thus the meaningful name change) manufactured and issued Mego's developed toy line. These products included 6" action figures based upon the *Rocky* series of movies and a group of 10" human-like Cats named *Fabulous Felines* (which according to their packaging were designed by former Mego president Martin Abrams). The company also issued a small offering of figures named *Lords of Light*. Simply reissued, *Micronauts* figures each came with a phosphorus stick which when activated caused a glow-in-the-dark effect. Unfortunately, all of these products sold poorly and were discontinued. The company went out of business a short time later.

Customized Mego Action Figures

One of the fastest growing segments of Mego action figure collecting is that of collectors making their own Mego style figures. During the 1970s and early 1980s, Mego produced many of the most popular literary, comic book, TV, and movie characters into action figure form. However, even with so many characters manufactured, Mego could not possibly produce every character desired by fans and collectors. Filling this void and taking advantage of the company's varied interchangeable body sizes, collectors have been filling their wants by making their very own customized action

Custom 8" Mego type action figures of
Batman's Commissioner Gordon, Two Face,
and Mr. Freeze.

figures. Some very talented individuals have even produced small production runs for resale and can accommodate fellow collector character wants.

Using common products available in most hobby and art supply shops, collectors have had much success changing existing Mego characters into new ones they desire. Utilizing inexpensive molding products, existing Mego heads can be modified into other characters and then repainted. For harder characters, many patient and gifted customizers have sculpted their own heads from scratch. Collectors finish off their new creations by sewing their own figure outfits and manufacturing custom accessories. While results vary, the majority of customized figures are of a very high quality. A few are so well done that they are hard to distinguish from a actual factory produced Mego figure.

Beware of Impostors!

The majority of customized Mego figures are produced by collectors for their own personal enjoyment. Those that are sold for profit are normally labeled as a customized figure and are priced as such. Customized figures should not be confused with actual Mego production figures. Beware of persons selling customized figures as prototypes or rare Mego characters. Familiarity with the information in this book as well as Mego manufacturing methods will aid in spotting misleading customized figures.

Chapter Three
Original Action Figures

Action Jackson
1972-1973

Mego's first serious venture into the competitive action figure arena was *Action Jackson*. The boldest man of adventure was marketed as an inexpensive alternative to *GI Joe*.

Collector Notes:

Outfits were first issued in packaging that featured a drawing on the front and later in plain generic red boxes.

The Ward's exclusive *Amigo* was available through their 1974 Christmas catalog and packaged in a plain brown box.

Action Jackson was available in the UK as *Johnny Jackson* and in Italy as *L'Amico Jackson*.

Irwin issued three licensed accessories in 1974.

AJ38 was also marketed as a *Planet of the Apes* playset.

In 1982 Mego planned to revive and update *Action Jackson* as a military character.

AJ03 and AJ01

AJ28 and AJ24

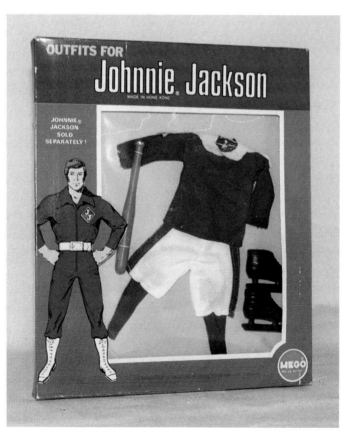

AJ43

AJ33

AJ35

AJ30

AJ32

AJ37

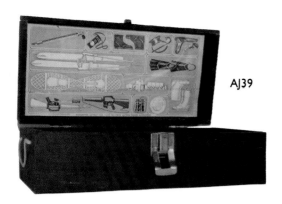

AJ39

AJ34

AJ36

AJ04 and AJ01

AJ20 and AJ05

39

AJ42

AJ44

AJ23

Toy Listings:

Name	Mint Value	MIB Value
(AJ01)AJ White	$10.00	$25.00
(AJ02)AJ Bearded	$10.00	$25.00
(AJ03)AJ Black	$25.00	$75.00
(AJ04)Amigo	$75.00	
(AJ05)Aussie Marine outfit	$3.00	$8.00
(AJ06)Air Force outfit	$3.00	$8.00
(AJ07)Navy outfit	$3.00	$8.00
(AJ08)Frogman outfit	$3.00	$8.00
(AJ09)Ski-Patrol outfit	$3.00	$8.00
(AJ10)Army outfit	$3.00	$8.00
(AJ11)Rescue Squad outfit	$3.00	$8.00
(AJ12)Western outfit	$3.00	$8.00
(AJ13)Scramble Cyclist outfit	$3.00	$8.00
(AJ14)Jungle Safari outfit	$3.00	$8.00
(AJ15)Secret Agent outfit	$3.00	$8.00
(AJ16)Snowmobile outfit	$3.00	$8.00
(AJ17)Fisherman outfit	$3.00	$8.00
(AJ18)Hockey outfit	$3.00	$8.00
(AJ19)Baseball outfit	$3.00	$8.00
(AJ20)Karate outfit	$3.00	$8.00
(AJ21)Football outfit	$3.00	$8.00
(AJ22)Surf and Scuba outfit	$3.00	$8.00
(AJ23)10 different blister outfits each:	$3.00	$8.00
(AJ24)Strap-on Helicopter accessory	$5.00	$15.00
(AJ25)Parachute Plunge accessory	$5.00	$15.00
(AJ26)Water Scooter accessory	$5.00	$15.00
(AJ27)Signal Searchlight accessory	NA	NP
(AJ28)Fire Rescue Pack	$5.00	$15.00
(AJ29)Scramble Cycle vehicle	$15.00	$35.00
(AJ30)Rescue Helicopter vehicle	$15.00	$50.00
(AJ31)Campmobile vehicle	$50.00	$125.00
(AJ32)Safari Jeep vehicle	$15.00	$50.00
(AJ33)Snow Mobile vehicle	$10.00	$35.00
(AJ34)Formula Racer vehicle	NSR	NSR
(AJ35)Wild Mustang Horse	$10.00	$50.00
(AJ36)Adventure Set includes AJ01,25,28,29		NSR
(AJ37)Jungle House playset	$30.00	$100.00
(AJ38)Lost Continent playset	$100.00	$350.00
(AJ39)Footlocker (Irwin)	$10.00	$40.00
(AJ40)Amphicat vehicle (Irwin)	$25.00	$75.00
(AJ41)Dune Buggy (Irwin)	$25.00	$75.00
(AJ42)AJ02 in Italian box	$10.00	$100.00
(AJ43)UK outfit	$5.00	$25.00
(AJ44)Walkie-Talkie Helmet	$20.00	$50.00

American West Series
1974-1975, 1980

With this series Mego tried its hand at issuing action figures based upon the fascinating real life characters of the old American west.

Collector Notes:
Figures were available to retailers first on Kresge style blister packs then in solid window boxes. Values differ, so they are listed individually for reference.

Figures were available in Germany as two-packs.

Mego reissued each figure on a Lion Rock blister card in 1980. Values are NSR each.

AW04

AW01 and AW12

AWI3

AW05 and AW06

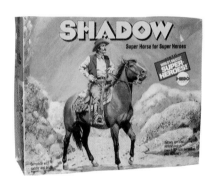

AWI7

AW08 and AW07

AW19

AW18

Toy Listings:

Name	Mint Value	MIB Value
(AW01)Wyatt Earp Kresge	$20.00	$100.00
(AW02)Wyatt Earp	$20.00	$60.00
(AW03)Buffalo Bill Kresge	$20.00	$100.00
(AW04)Buffalo Bill	$20.00	$60.00
(AW05)Sitting Bull Kresge	$20.00	$100.00
(AW06)Sitting Bull	$20.00	$60.00
(AW07)Wild Bill Hickock Kresge	$20.00	$100.00
(AW08)Wild Bill Hickock	$20.00	$60.00
(AW09)Cochise Kresge	$20.00	$100.00
(AW10)Cochise	$20.00	$60.00
(AW11)Davy Crockett Kresge	$20.00	$100.00
(AW12)Davy Crockett	$20.00	$60.00
(AW13)Figures on Blister Card each:	$20.00	$NSR
(AW14)German Two-Pack AW01,02	$40.00	$200.00
(AW15)German Two-Pack AW03,04	$40.00	$200.00
(AW16)German Two-Pack AW05,06	$40.00	$200.00
(AW17)Shadow	$35.00	$100.00
(AW18)Dodge City	NSR	NSR
(AW19)Store Display	NSR	NSR

C.B. McCaul
1977-1978

3 3/4" Action figures produced to take advantage of the then C.B. craze that briefly took the nation by storm. Each vehicle came with a microphone and voice amplifier.

Collector Notes:

All *C.B. McHaul* action figures and vehicles were ordered lightly by retailers, making them very difficult to find.

Action figures were packaged on *Comic Action Hero* style blister cards.

CB11

CB01-CB10

CB15

CB12

Toy Listings:

Name	Mint Value	MIB Value
(CB01)C.B.McHaul	$5.00	$20.00
(CB02)Jim Oakes	$5.00	$20.00
(CB03)Kidd Watts	$5.00	$20.00
(CB04)Joe Marconi	$5.00	$20.00
(CB05)Prof. Braine	$5.00	$20.00
(CB07)Bad Leroy	$5.00	$20.00
(CB08)Sgt. Brown	$5.00	$20.00
(CB09)Scowling Jack Jones	$5.00	$20.00
(CB10)Speed Johnson	$5.00	$20.00
(CB11)Trooper Car includes CH08, CH09	$20.00	$60.00
(CB12)C.B.McHaul's Rig includes CH01	$20.00	$60.00
(CB13)Bear Masher includes CH05,CH06	$20.00	$60.00
(CB14)Highway Wrecker	UKN	UKN
(CB15)Truck Stop (Sears only)	NSR	NSR

Commander Zack Power
1975-1976

6 1/2" figure with battery operated launcher and motorcycle. Was designed to compete with Ideal's popular *Evel Knievel* motorcycle and action figures.

CP01

CP01

Toy Listings:

Name	Mint Value	MIB Value
(CP01) 6 1/2" figure with motorcycle	$50.00	$150.00

Dare Brothers
1975

Flying glider toy with two 6" figures that were designed to be used outdoors. Other *Dare Brother* type toys were proposed but never implemented.

DB01

Reach the heights with the Dare Bros.

10⁷⁷ set

Launch the Dare Brothers into the air on their colorful, plastic fly glider and watch them defy death. As one brother holds onto the ankle straps of the other nestled under the 40-in. wide wing span of the glider, watch them scream and soar across the open skies up to 50 yds. depending on wind currents. Truly the action toy of the year. Set comes complete with two muscular 8-in. tall poseable Dare Brothers in bright leotards, long distance spring-action launcher, fly glider, and ankle straps. Not recommended for children under 5 years old.
48 T 24724—Ship. wt. 2 lbs...................................set 10.77

Toy Listings:

Name	Mint Value	MIB Value
(DB01)Fly Glider set with figures	NSR	NSR

Dr. Kromedome: The Bionic Villain
1975

Montgomery Wards wanted a villain to battle Kenner's Six Million Dollar man action figure. Since a Kenner villain was not yet available, Mego filled this void by producing 12" *Dr. Kromedome* as a Wards exclusive.

DK01

DK01

Toy Listings:

Name	Mint Value	MIB Value
(DK01)Dr. Kromedome (Wards)	$100.00	$250.00

Eagle Force
1982

2 3/4"*Eagle Force* was Mego's response to the successful reintroduction of Hasbro's new 3 3/4" *GI Joe*. Figures were made of diecast metal.

Collector Notes:
Mego granted HG Toys the rights to produce two play toy sets.

EF01-EF09

EF10-EF18

EF32

Eagle Force Commando Assault Set

Toy Listings:

Name	Mint Value	MIB Value
(EF01)Capt. Eagle	$1.00	$5.00
(EF02)Goldie Hawk	$3.00	$10.00
(EF03)Sgt. Brown	$1.00	$5.00
(EF04)Kayo	$1.00	$5.00
(EF05)Zapper	$1.00	$5.00
(EF06)Harley	$1.00	$5.00
(EF07)The Cat	$1.00	$5.00
(EF08)Redwing	$1.00	$5.00
(EF09)Stryker	$1.00	$5.00
(EF10)Big Bro	$1.00	$5.00
(EF11)Wild Bill	$1.00	$5.00
(EF12)Turk	$1.00	$5.00
(EF13)Baron Von Chill	$2.00	$10.00
(EF14)Shock Trooper	$2.00	$10.00
(EF15)Savitar	$2.00	$10.00
(EF16)Beta Man	$2.00	$10.00
(EF17)General Mamba	$2.00	$10.00
(EF18)Nemisis	$2.00	$10.00
(EF19)Bivouac Adventure Pack with EF12	$8.00	$15.00
(EF20)Tactical Adventure Pack with EF03	$8.00	$15.00
(EF21)Communications Pack with EF05	$8.00	$15.00
(EF22)Ocean Patrol Pack with EF08	$8.00	$15.00
(EF24)Eagle Island playset with EF03-8	$35.00	$55.00
(EF25)Eagle Island playset	$20.00	$40.00
(EF26)Talon Tank	$20.00	$40.00
(EF27)Fighter Plane	$20.00	$40.00
(EF28)Motorcycle with sidecar	UKN	UKN
(EF29)Eliminator Jeep	$10.00	$25.00
(EF30)Rampage Tank	$20.00	$40.00
(EF31)Bushwacker Jeep	$10.00	$25.00
(EF32)Command Assault Set (HG Toys)	$20.00	$40.00
(EF33)Tank Commander Set (HG Toys)	$20.00	$40.00

Fighting Yank and Richie
1970-1973

12" Generic military and civilian action figure designed as a low-cost alternative to GI Joe.

Collector Notes:
Montgomery Ward issued exclusive Fighting Yank figures named Hombre, The Baron, and Yankee Bravo. These were only available in brown shipping boxes through their 1973 mail order catalog.

The Systems Control Headquarters playset was also a Ward exclusive and only available in a brown shipping box.

FY01

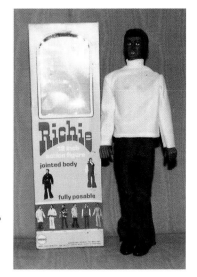

FY16

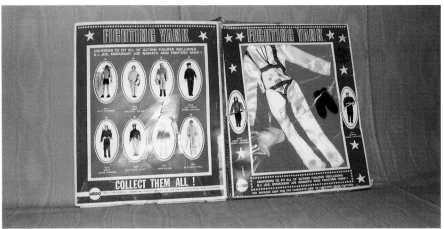

FY08

FY03, FY02, FY04

Toy Listings:

Name	Mint Value	MIB Value
(FY01)Fighting Yank	$10.00	$35.00
(FY02)Hombre (Wards)	NSR	NSR
(FY03)The Baron (Wards)	NSR	NSR
(FY04)Yankee Bravo (Wards)	NSR	NSR
(FY05)Frogman outfit	$2.00	$10.00
(FY06)MP outfit	$2.00	$10.00
(FY07)Flight outfit	$2.00	$10.00
(FY08)Air Force outfit	$2.00	$10.00
(FY09)Marine Dress outfit	$2.00	$10.00
(FY10)Special Forces outfit	$2.00	$10.00
(FY11)Navy Dress outfit	$2.00	$10.00
(FY12)West Point Cadet outfit	$2.00	$10.00
(FY13)Snowbound outfit	$2.00	$10.00
(FY14)Ski Patrol outfit	$2.00	$10.00
(FY15)Systems Control Headquarter (Wards)	NSR	NSR
(FY16)Richie	$10.00	$35.00
(FY17)Richie Black	$10.00	$35.00

Frankenbumps Monster
1982

15" Stretch type figure of the monster Frankenstein. Came with a hand pump which could distort its shape when filled with air.

FM01

Toy Listings:

Name	Mint Value	MIB Value
(FM01)Monster	UKN	UKN

Knights
1975-1976

Beautiful set of detailed 8" action figures based on the legend of Camelot and the Knights of the Round Table.

Collector Notes:
    Never produced Knights Castle was issued as the Sears exclusive *Wizard of Oz Wicked Witch Castle.*
    Guenevere was planned but never issued.

KN05 and KN04

KN01 and KN02

KN02, KN03, KN01

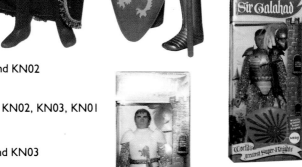

KN05 and KN03

KN07 and KN08

Toy Listings:

Name	Mint Value	MIB Value
(KN01)King Arthur	$35.00	$95.00
(KN02)Launcelot	$45.00	$100.00
(KN03)Sir Galahad	$35.00	$95.00
(KN04)Ivanhoe	$35.00	$95.00
(KN05)Black Knight	$65.00	$150.00
(KN06)Guenevere	NP	NP
(KN07)Castle playset	NP	NP
(KN08)Jousting Horse	UKN	UKN

Mad Monsters
1974-1975, 1980

Very popular at the time of their introduction and with collectors today. While not licensed, these high quality figures are sometimes referred to as *Universal Monsters*.

Collector Notes:
Figures have been found on Kresge style blister cards and in both solid and window box packaging styles. They were reissued on blister cards that say Lion Rock rather then Mego on them. Prices vary so they are individually listed.

Frankenstein and Dracula have been found with different facial and hair coloring suggesting the use of two different molds used during manufacturing. Prices are NSR for these variations.

MM13 and MM08

MM11 and MM02

MM17

Toy Listings:

Name	Mint Value	MIB Value
(MM01)Frankenstein Kresge card	$25.00	$250.00
(MM02)Frankenstein solid box	$25.00	$75.00
(MM03)Frankenstein window box	$25.00	$250.00
(MM04)Frankenstein Lion Rock	$25.00	$150.00
(MM05)Dracula Kresge card	$30.00	$250.00
(MM06)Dracula solid box	$35.00	$95.00
(MM07)Dracula window box	$30.00	$250.00
(MM08)Dracula Lion Rock	$30.00	$150.00
(MM09)Wolfman Kresge card	$30.00	$250.00
(MM10)Wolfman sold box	$35.00	$95.00
(MM11)Wolfman window box	$30.00	$250.00
(MM12)Wolfman Lion Rock	$30.00	$150.00
(MM13)Mummy Kresge card	$25.00	$250.00
(MM14)Mummy sold box	$25.00	$75.00
(MM15)Mummy window box	$25.00	$250.00
(MM16)Mummy Lion Rock	$25.00	$150.00
(MM17)Mad Monster Castle	$150.00	$400.00

Micronauts
1977-1982

Mego successfully re-engineered a popular Japanese toy line called *Microman* into one of its greatest successes.

Collector Notes:
Early figures featured Japanese detailing and trademark information.
3 3/4" Figures were issued in different colors to stimulate multiple sales.
Nichols Toys produced licensed Micronaut play toys.

MI23

MI39 and MI03

MI42 and MI59

MI61 and MI60

Ml40 and Ml41

Ml77 and Ml75

Ml28

MI72 and MI63

MI26 and MI27

MI24 and MI25

MI70 and MI71

MI51

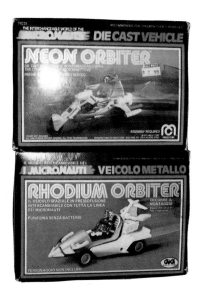

MI34 and MI32

MI80

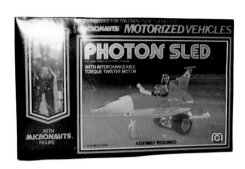

MI15

MI76

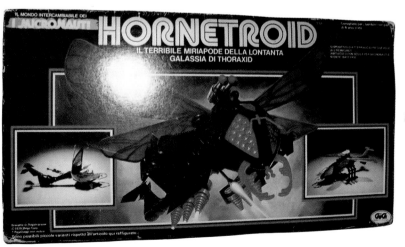

MI50

63

MI79

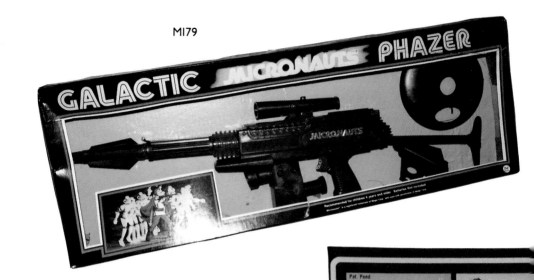

MI35, MI36, MI68, MI57

MI66

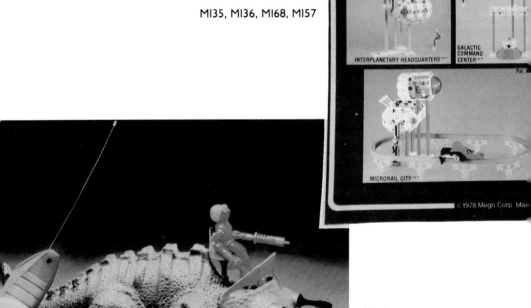

MI65

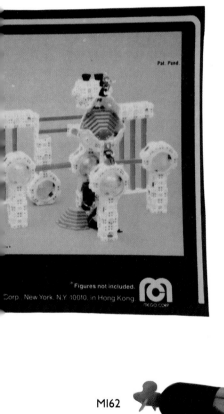

MI62

Toy Listings:

Name	Mint Value	MIB Value
First Series:		
(MI01)3 3/4" Time Traveler red	$5.00	$15.00
(MI02)3 3/4" Space Glider	$5.00	$25.00
(MI03)3 3/4" Galactic Warrior	$5.00	$25.00
(MI04)3 3/4" Acroyear	$5.00	$25.00
(MI05)8" Microtron	$30.00	$65.00
(MI06)12" Biotron	$30.00	$75.00
(MI07)Galactic Cruiser	$30.00	$65.00
(MI08)Hydra	$15.00	$35.00
(MI09)Gyro Tron	NP	NP
(MI10)Hydra Copter	$10.00	$25.00
(MI11)Ultronic Scooter	$5.00	$25.00
(MI13)Ultronic Scooter with MI01		$25.00
(MI14)Photon Sled	$5.00	NSR
(MI15)Photon Sled with MI01		$25.00
(MI16)Warp Racer	$5.00	NSR
(MI17)Warp Racer with MI01		$25.00
(MI18)Crater Cruncher	$5.00	NSR
(MI19)Crater Cruncher with MI01		$25.00
(MI20)Stratostation	$20.00	$45.00
(MI21)Astrostation	$20.00	$45.00
Second Series:		
(MI22)3 3/4" Acroyear II	$10.00	$25.00
(MI23)3 3/4" Pharoid	$10.00	$25.00
(MI24)8" Baron Karza	$35.00	$100.00
(MI25)8" Andromeda	$20.00	$75.00
(MI26)8" Force Commander	$35.00	$100.00
(MI27)8" Oberon	$20.00	$75.00
(MI28)8" Nemesis	$25.00	$75.00
(MI29)8" Giant Acroyear	$30.00	$85.00
(MI30)12" Phobos	$45.00	$100.00
(MI31)Battle Cruiser	$35.00	$75.00
(MI32)Rhodium Orbiter	$15.00	$45.00
(MI33)Thorium Orbiter	$15.00	$45.00
(MI34)Neon Orbiter	$15.00	$45.00
(MI35)Interplanetary Headquarters	NSR	NSR
(MI36)Galactic Command Center	NSR	NSR
(MI37)Monorail City	NSR	NSR
(MI38)Space Vehicle with MI01 (Wards only)	NSR	NSR
Third Series:		
(MI39)3 3/4" Galactic Defender	$15.00	$35.00
(MI40)3 3/4" Membros	$25.00	$75.00
(MI41)3 3/4" Antron	$25.00	$75.00
(MI42)3 3/4" Repto	$25.00	$75.00
(MI43)Mobile Exploration Lab	$20.00	$50.00
(MI44)Aquatron	$10.00	$25.00
(MI45)Galactic Cruiser	$10.00	$25.00

(MI46)Rocket Tubes	NSR	NSR
(MI47)Deluxe Rocket Tubes	$50.00	$200.00
Fourth Series:		
(MI48)Solarion	$15.00	$35.00
(MI49)Taurion	$15.00	$35.00
(MI50)Hornetroid	$50.00	$100.00
(MI51)Terraphant	$50.00	$125.00
(MI52)Alphatron	$10.00	$25.00
(MI53)Gammatron	$10.00	$25.00
(MI54)Betatron	$10.00	$25.00
(MI55)Star Searcher	$45.00	$100.00
(MI56)Karrio	$20.00	$50.00
(MI57)Mega City	NSR	NSR
(MI58)Survey Station (JCPenny only)	NSR	NSR
Fifth Series:		
(MI59)3 3/4" Centaurus	$40.00	$100.00
(MI60)3 3/4" Kronos	$40.00	$100.00
(MI61)3 3/4" Lobros	$40.00	$100.00
(MI62)Sharkos	NSR	NSR
(MI63)Ampzilla	$250.00	$600.00
(MI64)Lobstros	UKN	UKN
(MI65)Equestron	NP	NP
(MI66)Iguanos	NP	NP
(MI67)Micropolis Megacity (JCPenny only)	NSR	NSR
(MI68)Microrail City	NSR	NSR
(MI69)Rocket Tubes with launch pad	$60.00	$150.00
Sixth Series:		
(MI70)8" Emperor	$100.00	$200.00
(MI71)8" Megas	$75.00	$150.00
(MI72)8" Green Baron	$100.00	$250.00
(MI73)8" Pegasus	$100.00	$150.00
(MI74)8" King Atlas	$150.00	$300.00
(MI75)8" Lanturan	$100.00	$250.00
(MI76)8" Red Falcon	$200.00	$500.00
(MI77)8" Blizzard	$100.00	$300.00
(MI78)Galactic Helmet(Nichols)	$20.00	$45.00
(MI79)Galactic Phazer(Nichols)	$20.00	$45.00
(MI80)Microtimer	$75.00	$150.00

One Million B.C.
1977-1978

A line of action figures based upon the always popular prehistoric theme. While the name was derived from the popular B movie of the same name, they are unrelated.

Collector Notes:

The head used for Mada was a reworked version of the head used for *The Waltons* mother.

All figures except Mada came with a foam spear and featured throwing arm action.

Dinosaurs featured "growling action."

OM01 and OM04

 OM02 and OM03

OM05

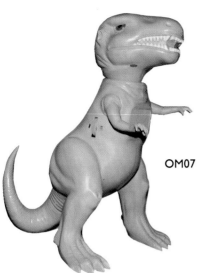

OM07

OM06

OM09

Toy Listings:

Name	Mint Value	MIB Value
(OM01)Trag	$20.00	$75.00
(OM02)Mada	$30.00	$95.00
(OM03)Zon	$30.00	$95.00
(OM04)Orm	$20.00	$75.00
(OM05)Grok	$20.00	$75.00
(OM06)Hairy Rhino	$200.00	$400.00
(OM07)Tyrannosaur	$200.00	$400.00
(OM08)Dimetroden	$200.00	$400.00
(OM09)Tribal Lair	NP	NP

Pirates
1975

Mego 8" action figures based upon the inherent popularity of pirates with children.

Collector Notes:
An unknown fifth pirate was originally conceived as part of this line but for unknown reasons was never produced.
A pirate castle was planned but never manufactured.

PI01 and PI04

PI04 and PI01

PI03 and PI02

PI02 and PI03

Toy Listings:

Name	Mint Value	MIB Value
(PI01)Black Beard	$35.00	$100.00
(PI02)Jean Lafitte	$40.00	$125.00
(PI03)Long John Silver	$40.00	$125.00
(PI04)Capt. Patch	$35.00	$100.00

Robin Hood
1975-1976

A beautiful and popular collector's line of 8" action figures based upon the legendary Robin Hood characters.

Collector Notes:

Rumors of a Sheriff of Nottingham and Maid Marion abound in Europe and Australia but none have been found to date.

A Nottingham Castle playset has been rumored as a European exclusive.

RH01 and RH04

RH04 and RH03

RH02 and RH01

RH02 and RH01

Toy Listings:

Name	Mint Value	MIB Value
(RH01)Robin Hood	$45.00	$125.00
(RH02)Little John	$25.00	$75.00
(RH03)Friar Tuck	$25.00	$75.00
(RH04)Will Scarlet	$60.00	$175.00

World War II Heroes
1976-1981

Mego produced this highly detailed line of 6" action figures specifically for the European toy market. Based upon the combat units that participated in World War II, each fully poseable figure came equipped with an authentic uniform, accessories, and was facially detailed to portray the country of origin. In 1980 select figures were finally introduced in America.

Collector Notes:

All figures are marked Lion Rock and issued only in window boxes.

Figures were issued in French, British, Italian, and US packaging. Values are the same.

It is currently unknown if vehicles or accessories were produced.

Figures were reissued by other companies on blister cards during the 1980s and significantly reduced in quality.

WH35 and WH30

WH08 and WH13

U.S. FIGHTER PILOT
PILOTE AMERICAIN
#74201/6

U.S. AIRFORCE TAIL GUNNER
MITRAILLEUR AMERICAIN
#74201/7

U.S. MARINE
MARINE AMERICAIN
#74201/8

SCOTS GUARD
GARDE ECOSSAIS
#74202/3

ANZAC BUSH FIGHTER
COMMANDO AUSTRALIEN
#74203/7

GERMAN INFANTRYMAN
FANTASSIN ALLEMAND
#74202/6

U.S. COMBAT OFFICER
OFFICIER AMERICAIN
#74201/4

BRITISH PARATROOPER
PARACHUTISTE ANGLAIS
#74202/7

WH01-WH36

U.S. FIGHTING SEABEE
SOLDAT DU GENIE NAVAL AMERICAIN
#74201/1

U.S. PARATROOPER
PARACHUTISTE AMERICAIN
#74201/2

FROGMAN
HOMME GRENOUILLE AMERICAIN
#74201/9

BRITISH TORPEDO BOAT CAPTAIN
COMMANDANT DE TORPILLEUR
ANGLAIS
#74202/1

GERMAN AFRIKA KORPS
AFRIKA KORPS
#74202/0

GERMAN PARATROOPER
PARACHUTISTE ALLEMAND
#74204/4

GERMAN MOUNTAIN TROOPER
CHASSEUR ALPIN ALLEMAND
#74204/3

RUSSIAN INFANTRYMAN
FANTASSIN RUSSE
#74205/1

RUSSIAN OFFICER
OFFICIER RUSSE
#74205/2

ITALIAN PARTISAN
PARTISAN ITALIEN
#74204/2

74

FANTRYMAN
SSIN AMERICAIN
5

U.S. ARCTIC INFANTRYMAN
INFANTERIE POLAIRE
#74201/0

H DESERT RAT
U DESERT ANGLAIS
2/9

BRITISH TANK COMMANDER
COMMANDANT DE TANK ANGLAIS
#74204/3

GERMAN U-BOAT COMMANDER
COMMANDANT DE SOUS MARIN
ALLEMAND   #74202/8

LUFTWAFFE PILOT
PILOTE ALLEMAND
#74202/4

FRENCH INFANTRYMAN
FANTASSIN FRANCAIS
#74205/3

UDER
O AMERICAIN

JAPANESE OFFICEH
OFFICIER JAPONAIS
#74203/2

JAPANESE SHARPSHOOTER
FRANC-TIREUR JAPONAIS

JAPANESE INFANTRYMAN
FANTASSIN JAPONAIS
#74203/4

MANDO
ANGLAIS

FRENCH TANK COMMANDER
COMMANDANT DE TANK FRANCAIS
#74205/4

FRENCH LEGIONNAIRE
LEGIONAIRE FRANCAIS
#74204/5

FRENCH RESISTANCE FIGHTER
RESISTANT FRANCAIS
#74202/5

JAPANESE FIGHTER PILOT
PILOTE JAPONAIS
#74203/3

CHINESE INFANTRYMAN
FANTASSIN CHINOIS
#74203/5

CHINESE GUERILLA FIGHTER
MAQUISARD CHINOIS
#74203/6

Toy Listings:

Name	Mint Value	MIB Value
US Military:		
(WH01)Fighting Seabee	$10.00	$55.00
(WH02)Paratrooper	$10.00	$55.00
(WH03)Marauder	$10.00	$55.00
(WH04)Combat Officer	$10.00	$55.00
(WH05)Infantryman	$10.00	$55.00
(WH06)Arctic Infantryman	$10.00	$55.00
(WH07)Fighter Pilot	$10.00	$55.00
(WH08)Airforce Tail Gunner	$10.00	$55.00
(WH09)Marine	$10.00	$55.00
(WH10)Frogman	NSR	NSR
British Military:		
(WH11)Torpedo Boat Captain	$10.00	$55.00
(WH12)Commando	$10.00	$55.00
(WH13)Paratrooper	$10.00	$55.00
(WH14)Desert Rat	$10.00	$55.00
(WH15)Tank Commander	$10.00	$55.00
(WH16)Scots Guard	$20.00	$85.00
(WH17)Anzac Bush Fighter	$10.00	$55.00
German Military:		
(WH18)Infantryman	$15.00	$75.00
(WH19)Afrika Korps	$15.00	$75.00
(WH20)Paratrooper	$15.00	$75.00
(WH21)Mountain Trooper	$15.00	$75.00
(WH22)U Boat Commander	$15.00	$75.00
(WH23)Luftwaffe Pilot	$20.00	$85.00
French Military:		
(WH24)Infantryman	$10.00	$55.00
(WH25)Tank Commander	$10.00	$55.00
(WH26)Legionnaire	$10.00	$55.00
(WH27)Resistance Fighter	$10.00	$55.00
Russian Military:		
(WH28)Infantryman	$10.00	$55.00
(WH29)Officer	$10.00	$55.00
Italian Military:		
(WH30)Partisan	$10.00	$55.00
Japanese Military:		
(WH31)Officer	$10.00	$55.00
(WH32)Sharpshooter	$10.00	$55.00
(WH33)Infantryman	$10.00	$55.00
(WH34)Fighter Pilot	$15.00	$75.00
Chinese Military:		
(WH35)Infantryman	$10.00	$55.00
(WH36)Guerrilla Fighter	$10.00	$55.00

Chapter Four
TV Action figures and Personalities

Muhammad Ali
1976-1977

Beautifully designed 9" line of action figures that never really caught on with children. Today are desired by not only action figure collectors but sport memorabilia collectors as well.

Collector Notes:
Exclusive figure with boxing accessories was available only in the UK.
Figures could simulate boxing by utilizing a spring mechanism with in each figure.

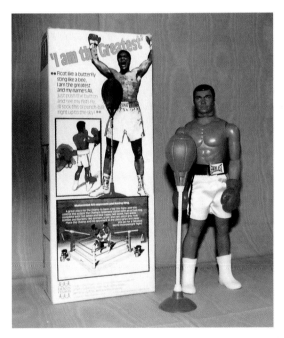

MA02

MA02

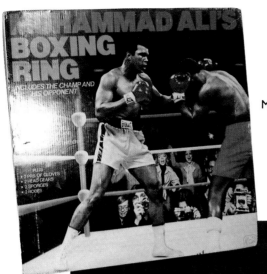

MA09

MA04-MA07

Toy Listings:

Name	Mint Value	MIB Value
(MA01)Muhammad Ali	$30.00	$95.00
(MA02)Muhammad Ali (UK only)	$30.00	$200.00
(MA03)Opponent	$20.00	$65.00
(MA04)Carrot Kid	NP	NP
(MA05)Lightning Lefty	NP	NP
(MA06)Battling Ben	NP	NP
(MA07)Manila Mauler	NP	NP
(MA08)Boxing Ring	UKN	UKN
(MA09)Boxing Ring includes MU01,03	$100.00	$250.00
(MU10)Boxing Gloves	$20.00	$75.00
(MU11)Bob Bag	NSR	NSR

Franz Beckenbauer
1976

Mego produced a 9" action figure of famed West German soccer player Franz Beckenbauer. Beckenbauer captained the winning West German World Cup team in 1974 and was European player of the year twice (1972, 1976) before starting a new soccer career in the United States with the North American Soccer League's New York Cosmos (1977-80, 1983).

Collector Notes:
Action figure was available exclusively in Germany. It is presently unknown if other soccer stars were produced.
Unknown if figure was issued in a box or blister card.
Figure features a "kicking leg" feature and is marked Lion Rock.

FB01

PB01

Toy Listings:

Name	Mint Value	MIB Value
(FB01)Franz Beckenbauer	$100.00	NSR

Broadway Joe Namath
1971-1972

Mego's first celebrity action figure was that of New York Jets famed 1969 Super Bowl Hero, Joe Namath.

Collector Notes:
Figure was available in a open face box with out cellophane or cardboard for protection. This could explain why many MIB figures today are missing their small brown football.

BJ01

BJ01

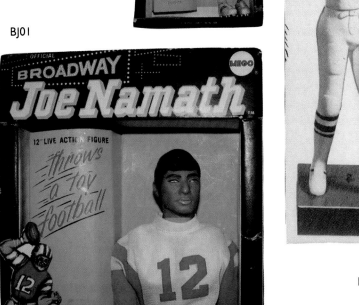

9020

BJ14

BJ14

Toy Listings:

Name	Mint Value	MIB Value
(BJ01)Broadway Joe action figure	$100.00	$300.00
(BJ02)Touchdown outfit	$10.00	$25.00
(BJ03)Bachelor outfit	$10.00	$25.00
(BJ04)Maximum Effort outfit	$10.00	$25.00
(BJ05)Backfield in Motion outfit	$10.00	$25.00
(BJ06)In Vest outfit	$10.00	$25.00
(BJ07)Reddog outfit	$10.00	$25.00
(BJ08)Different Drummer outfit	$10.00	$25.00
(BJ09)Eligible Receiver outfit	$10.00	$25.00
(BJ10)Tuff Tux outfit	$10.00	$25.00
(BJ11)Double Coverage outfit	$10.00	$25.00
(BJ12)Furward Pass outfit	$10.00	$25.00
(BJ13)Jet Set outfit	$10.00	$25.00
(BJ14)20" Joe Namath Football Passer	NSR	NSR

Chips
1978-1982

Mego went back to its TV roots with its 3 3/4" and 8"*Chips* action figures. While not a major toy hit, *Chips* action figures were a steady seller for Mego.

Collector Notes:

Notably absent from the Chips 8" line up was a villain. Chopper from *Starsky and Hutch* was shown as a *Chips* villain at the 1979 Toy Fair but never issued.

Empire Toys issued a *Chips* Van and Helicopter that were not sanctioned by Mego.

CH10 and CH11

CH11 and CH12

CH13

CH02 and CH01

CH16

Toy Listings:

Name	Mint Value	MIB Value
3 3/4" Action Figures:		
(CH01)Jon	$3.00	$10.00
(CH02)Ponch	$3.00	$10.00
(CH03)Sarge	$3.00	$10.00
(CH04)Wheels Willy	$3.00	$10.00
(CH05)Jimmy Squeaks	$3.00	$10.00
(CH06)Motorcycle	$5.00	$15.00
(CH07)Jon with Motorcycle		NSR
(CH08)Ponch with Motorcycle		NSR
(CH09)Sarge with Police Car	$30.00	$75.00
8" Action Figures:		
(CH10)Jon	$10.00	$25.00
(CH11)Ponch	$10.00	$25.00
(CH12)Sarge	$15.00	$30.00
(CH13)Motorcycle	$20.00	$50.00
(CH14)Helicopter (Empire Toys)	$20.00	$55.00
(CH15)Van (Empire Toys)	$20.00	$55.00
(CH16)Motorcycle with launcher	$5.00	$15.00

Dallas
1981

Mego proposed a line of 3 3/4" action figures based on the late night soap opera. Retailers felt that the adult nature of the show would not interest children and did not place enough orders to warrant production.

Collector Notes:

To date no authentic *Dallas* action figures have been found by collectors.

DA01-DA09

Toy Listings:

Name	Mint Value	MIB Value
(DA01)JR	NP	NP
(DA02)Bobby	NP	NP
(DA03)Jock	NP	NP
(DA04)Miss Ellie	NP	NP
(DA05)Sue Ellen	NP	NP
(DA06)Pamela	NP	NP
(DA07)Lucy	NP	NP
(DA08)Card Game	$5.00	$15.00
(DA09)Dart Game	$10.00	$25.00

Dr. Who
1977-1978

Mego produced a line of 9" action figures based on the long running *Dr. Who* British science fiction television series. Featuring some of Mego's best design work, *Dr. Who* figures were a success then and are avidly collected by fans today.

Collector Notes:
Made exclusively for the British retail market, the Dr. Who figure itself was also available in Italy.

Character additions of the Master and Davros were planned but never produced.

DW04

DW01 and DW03

DW05

DW06 and DW02

DW07

DW01 and DW07

DW06 and DW03

Toy Listings:

Name	Mint Value	MIB Value
(DW01)Dr. Who	$100.00	$250.00
(DW02)Leela	$100.00	$250.00
(DW03)K9	$200.00	$500.00
(DW04)Dalek	$150.00	$400.00
(DW05)Giant Robot	$150.00	$400.00
(DW06)Cyberman	$150.00	$400.00
(DW07)Tardis playset	$100.00	$275.00

The Dukes of Hazard
1981-1982

Mego's last major action figure hit before their bankruptcy. The success of the *Dukes of Hazard* TV series took Mego and retailers by surprise with toy shortages reported during its first year.

Collector Notes:

A General Lee scaled for the 8" figures was planned but never produced.

When the actors who played Bo and Luke left the show, Mego issued their figures with new heads of replacement characters Coy and Vance.

Cards remained the same.

In 1982, the company had planned to offer outfits for their 8" Daisy Duke on blister cards.

DH29 and DH30

DH26 and DH27

DH24, DH25, DH26, DH30

DH16-DH19

89

DH23

Toy Listings:

Name	Mint Value	MIB Value
3 3/4" Action Figures:		
(DH01)Bo	$5.00	$10.00
(DH02)Luke	$5.00	$10.00
(DH03)Daisy (heavy body)	NSR	NSR
(DH04)Daisy (slim body)	$5.00	$10.00
(DH05)Boss Hogg	$10.00	$25.00
(DH06)Sheriff Rosco	$10.00	$25.00
(DH07)Cooter	$10.00	$25.00
(DH08)Cletus	$10.00	$25.00
(DH09)Uncle Jesse	$10.00	$25.00
(DH10)Coy (card says Bo)	$10.00	$25.00
(DH11)Vance (card says Luke)	$10.00	$25.00
(DH12)Miz Tizdale	NP	NP
(DH13)Hughie Hogg	NP	NP
(DH14)Flash	NP	NP
(DH15)Sheriff Little	NP	NP
(DH16)General Lee with DH01,2	$10.00	$35.00
(DH17)Jeep with DH04	$10.00	$35.00
(DH18)Caddy with DH05	NSR	NSR
(DH19)Police Car with DH06	NSR	NSR
(DH20)Motorized Crash Set playset	NP	NP
(DH21)General Lee Crash Car	NP	NP
(DH22)Caddy Crash Car	NP	NP
(DH23)Cooters Garage playset	NP	NP
8" Action Figures:		
(DH24)Bo	$10.00	$35.00
(DH25)Luke	$10.00	$35.00
(DH26)Daisy (blue shirt)	$10.00	$35.00
(DH27)Daisy (green shirt)	$10.00	$35.00
(DH28)Vance (card says Luke)	$20.00	$75.00
(DH29)Coy (card says Bo)	$20.00	$75.00
(DH30)Boss Hogg	$10.00	$35.00

Flash Gordon
1978

Based upon the famed comic strip of the same name. These 9" figures are some of the best ever designed by Mego.

FG01 and FG02

FG04 and FG03

FG05

Toy Listings:

Name	Mint Value	MIB Value
(FG01)Flash Gordon	$40.00	$100.00
(FG02)Dale Arden	$50.00	$125.00
(FG03)Ming	$50.00	$125.00
(FG04)Zarkoff	$40.00	$100.00
(FG05)Flash Gordon Playset	$55.00	$125.00

The Flintstones
1977

Extremely rare offering based on the popular Hanna Barbera stone age family.

Collector Notes:

Originally 5 1/2" figures and accessories were going to be made available individually on blister cards.

Playset included Fred, Wilma, Barney, Betty, and Dino.

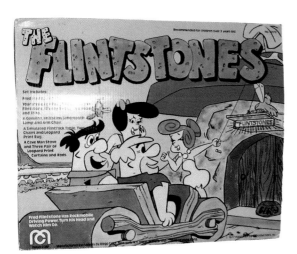

FL01

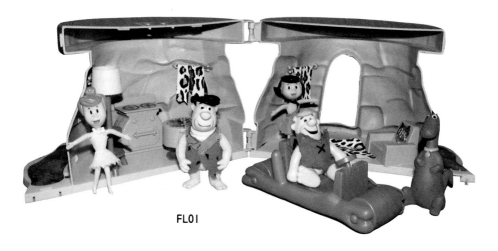

FL01

FL01

Toy Listings:

Name	Mint Value	MIB Value
(FL01)Flinstones' Playset	$300.00	$600.00

The Greatest American Hero
1982

Mego had high hopes that 3 3/4" and 8" action figures based upon this successful television show would sell well. Unfortunately, the company went of business before the majority of these toys could be manufactured and issued.

Collector Notes:
Authentic prototypes of Ralph and Bill are owned by collectors.

The Greatest American Hero™ is one of the greatest American TV shows…so you can't miss with this new Mego® series of funmakers!

GA02-GA04

22001 The Greatest American Hero™ 8" Costumed and Poseable Figures: Ralph,™ Bill™ and Pam™
The zaniest super-hero ever to hit the toy scene!

Kids love him because he's goofy. Can he save the world? With the help of Pam, his TV girlfriend…and Special agent Bill…they mix it up for the funniest time ever!

© 1981 Stephen J. Cannell Productions

Where would The Greatest American Hero™ be without the Convertible Bug? So you can make a kid's dreams come true with a replica—direct from the top rated TV show!

GA01

22010 The Greatest American Hero™ Free-Wheeling Convertible Bug With Ralph™ and Bill™ (3¾")
The free-wheeling convertible, a favorite with

every kid, right from the hit TV series. Now with two exciting action figures—Ralph and Bill—that kids can pose in endless ways that play out their fantasies.

© 1981 Stephen J. Cannell Productions

GA01

GA05

Toy Listings:

Name	Mint Value	MIB Value
3 3/4" Action Figures:		
(GA01) Car with Ralph and Bill	$100.00	$250.00
8" Action Figures:		
(GA02)Ralph	NP	NP
(GA03)Bill	NP	NP
(GA04)Pam	NP	NP
(GA05)Ralph prototype	$1800.00	

Happy Days
1977-1978

8" action figures based upon the long running hit TV series. If the line became a major success, Mego had planned new character introductions and an additional playset.

Collector Notes:

Fonzie featured "thumbs up" action and was the most popular action figure.

Fonzie was also issued as a 15" cloth rag doll manufactured by the Mego subsidiary Samet and Wells.

The Happy Days action figure television commercial featured a 8" unknown female character which was not made available.

HD04 and HD05

HD01

HD02 and HD03

HD07

HD09

HD06

HD08

Toy Listings:

Name	Mint Value	MIB Value
(HD01)Richie	$20.00	$50.00
(HD02)Potsy	$20.00	$50.00
(HD03)Ralph	$20.00	$50.00
(HD04)Fonzie (boxed)	$20.00	$50.00
(HD05)Fonzie (carded)	$20.00	$60.00
(HD06)Hot Rod	$25.00	$60.00
(HD07)Garage playset	$60.00	$150.00
(HD08)15" Fonzie cloth	$10.00	
(HD09)Fonzie Motorcycle	$15.00	$50.00

Kiss
1978-1980

These incredible detailed 12" figures are based on the hard rock group of the same name.

KS06-KS09

KS01-KS04

KS05

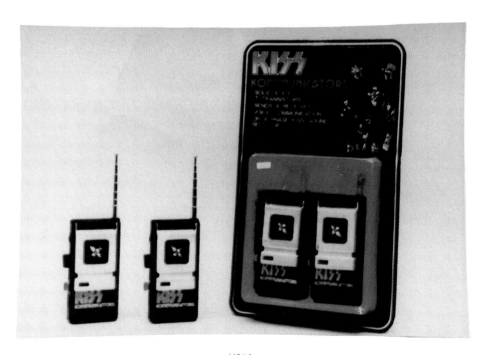

KS10

Toy Listings:

Name	Mint Value	MIB Value
(KS01)Paul Stanley	$50.00	$125.00
(KS02)Gene Simmons	$50.00	$125.00
(KS03)Peter Criss	$50.00	$125.00
(KS04)Ace Frehley	$65.00	$150.00
(KS05)Camping Set	NP	NP
(KS06)5 1/2" Paul bendy	NP	NP
(KS07)5 1/2" Gene bendy	NP	NP
(KS08)5 1/2" Peter bendy	NP	NP
(KS09)5 1/2" Ace bendy	NP	NP
(KS10)Kommunicators	UKN	UKN

Laverne and Shirley
1978

Set of four 12" action figures based on the Happy Days spin-off series *Laverne and Shirley*.

Collector Notes:
8" figures were first considered so that the figures could be compatible with the similarly themed *Happy Days* action figures.

Figures were available only in two-packs.

LS01

LS02

LS02

Toy Listings:

Name	Mint Value	MIB Value
(LS01)Laverne and Shirley	$50.00	$125.00
(LS02)Lenny and Squiggy	$50.00	$125.00

The Love Boat
1982

3 3/4" figures based upon the popular TV series.

Collector Notes:
Figures were issued with or without knee joints.

LB02, LB06, LB05

LB01-LB06

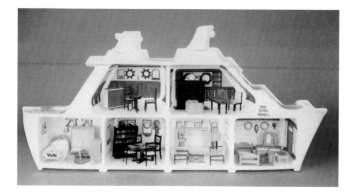

LB07

Toy Listings:

Name	Mint Value	MIB Value
(LB01)Capt. Stubing	$2.00	$10.00
(LB02)Vicki	$2.00	$10.00
(LB03)Gopher	$2.00	$10.00
(LB04)Isaac	$2.00	$10.00
(LB05)Julie	$2.00	$10.00
(LB06)Doc	$2.00	$10.00
(LB07)Love Boat playset	UKN	UKN
(LB08)Love Boat playset with figures	UKN	UKN
(LB09)Doc office set	NP	NP
(LB10)Capt. Quarters set	NP	NP
(LB11)Julie's Room set	NP	NP
(LB12)Doc's office set	NP	NP
(LB13)Guest Room set	NP	NP
(LB14)Dining Room set	NP	NP
(LB15)Isaac Bar set —	NP	NP

The New Avengers
1977

Aborted UK only 12" action figure line based upon the updated version of the classic 1960s television series *The Avengers*.

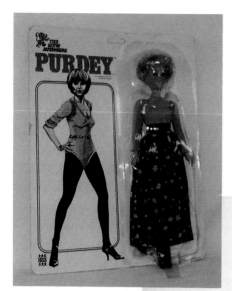

NA01

NA09 and NA10

Steed and Gambit

Dressed in his smart suit, bowler hat and carrying that famous umbrella, the John Steed 11½" figure is ready for action-packed adventures! With a pull of the handle, Steed's umbrella converts amazingly to a sword stick and, by operating a button in his back, Steed's fencing arm lunges forward with a cut and thrust action!

The features of the handsome Avenger, Gambit, are captured in this super 11½" action figure! Ready for adventure, Gambit is dressed in his white karate suit which displays his black belt to the full!

By pressing a button in Gambit's back he will deliver a 'stunning' karate chop!

Toy Listings:

Name	Mint Value	MIB Value
(NA01)Purdy	$95.00	$300.00
(NA02)Cream Suit outfit	NSR	NSR
(NA03)Trouser Suit outfit	NSR	NSR
(NA04)Black Dress outfit	NSR	NSR
(NA05)Cream Suit outfit	NSR	NSR
(NA06)Jump Suit outfit	NSR	NSR
(NA07)Cat Suit outfit	NSR	NSR
(NA08)Halter Dress outfit	NSR	NSR
(NA09)John Steed	NP	NP
(NA10)Gambit	NP	NP

Our Gang
1977

With the *Our Gang* series of comedy shorts syndicated nationwide, Mego introduced this complete line of 6" action figures and playsets. Unfortunately retailers ordered lightly, prematurely ending the life of this well crafted line.

Collector Notes:
Club House playset included Petey the dog.

OG01-OG03

OG04-0G06

OG08

OG09

OG07

Toy Listings:

Name	Mint Value	MIB Value
(OG01)Spanky	$25.00	$75.00
(OG02)Alfalfa	$25.00	$75.00
(OG03)Porky	$25.00	$75.00
(OG04)Mickey	$25.00	$75.00
(OG05)Darla	$35.00	$95.00
(OG06)Buckwheat	$35.00	$95.00
(OG07)Club House	$50.00	$125.00
(OG08)Paddle Boat	$25.00	$65.00
(OG09)Orange Crate car	$25.00	$65.00

Space 1999
1976-1978

Mego could not issue action figures based on this science fiction television series in the US because Mattel Toys had already acquire the US rights. As a result the company obtained the TV shows foreign rights and issued a complete line of figures in Britain.

SP03 and SP01

SP05 and SP04

SP02

Toy Listings:

Name	Mint Value	MIB Value
(SP01)Captain Koenig	$75.00	$250.00
(SP02)Alan Carter	$150.00	$450.00
(SP03)Paul Morrow	$75.00	$250.00
(SP04)Mysterious Alien	$50.00	$125.00
(SP05)Capt. Zantor	$50.00	$125.00

Starsky and Hutch
1978-1979

A popular line of 8" figures based on the hit crime fighting television series.

Collector Notes:

Starsky and Hutch were available in the UK on single cards or two packs. Two pack figures came with pistols.

Police car was available in the UK without "twist out" action mechanism.

SH06 and SH07

SH05 and SH03

SH08

SH09

British advertisement for *Starsky and Hutch* figures and car.

Toy Listings:

Name	Mint Value	MIB Value
(SH01)Starsky	$10.00	$25.00
(SH02)Hutch	$10.00	$25.00
(SH03)Huggy Bear	$15.00	$35.00
(SH04)Dobey	$20.00	$45.00
(SH05)Chopper	$20.00	$45.00
(SH06)Starsky UK Card	$10.00	$50.00
(SH07)Hutch UK Card	$10.00	$50.00
(SH08)Two-pack UK only	$20.00	$125.00
(SH09)Police Car	$35.00	$75.00
(SH10)Police Car	NSR	NSR
(SH11)Alley Playset	NP	NP

Star Trek
1975-1977, 1979

High quality 8" action figure line based upon the classic *Star Trek* television series. Mego, *Star Trek*, and action figure collectors in general have made these figures some of the most desired of all Mego toys.

Collector Notes:

Chekov, Sulu, and Harry Mudd were designed but not manufactured.

A set of *Bend 'n Flex* figures were planned but never produced.

Kirk, McCoy, and Klingon were reissued in 1979. Card backs are blank and white.

The Intergalactic Planetarium came with a Starfleet Guide to the Solar System audio tape.

Tricorder came with an audio tape which contained an actual Star Trek episode.

ST27 through ST34 were science kits.

ST01 and ST02

ST05

ST03 and ST06

ST04 and ST09

ST10 and ST08

112

ST12 and ST13

ST07-ST14

ST15

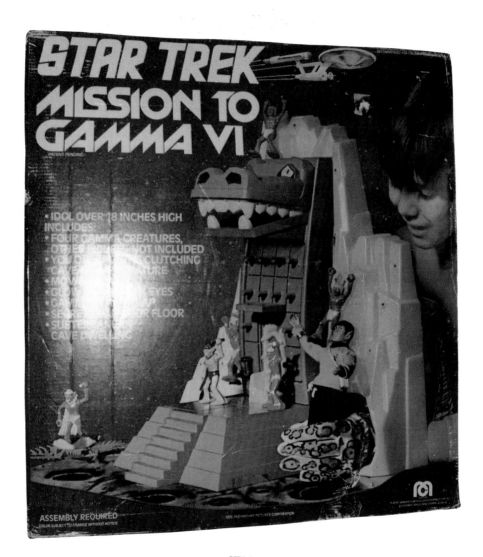

ST16

ST15

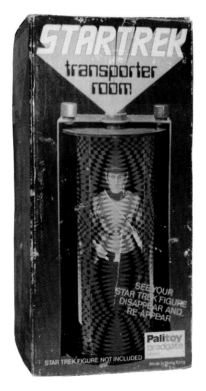

ST17

116

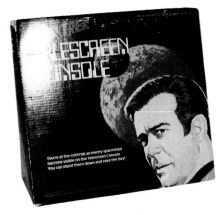

ST18

ST35

Package artwork from ST35
featuring Sulu and Chekov.

ST23

ST20

ST25

ST19

ST23

ST19

ST34

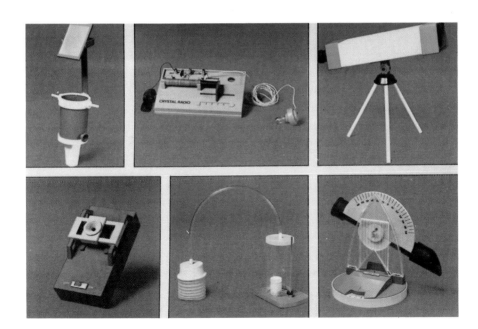

ST27-ST33

Toy Listings:

Name	Mint Value	MIB Value
First Series:		
(ST01)Kirk	$20.00	$60.00
(ST02)Spock	$20.00	$60.00
(ST03)McCoy	$20.00	$60.00
(ST04)Scotty	$35.00	$95.00
(ST05)Klingon	$35.00	$95.00
Series Two:		
(ST06)Uhura	$35.00	$95.00
Series Three:		
(ST07)Keeper	$60.00	$150.00
(ST08)Gorn	$80.00	$175.00
(ST09)Neptunian	$80.00	$175.00
(ST10)Cheron	$60.00	$150.00
Series Four:		
(ST11)Talos	$125.00	$300.00
(ST12)Romulan	$350.00	$800.00
(ST13)Mugato	$175.00	$350.00
(ST14)Andorian	$250.00	$500.00
(ST15)USS Enterprise	$75.00	$150.00
(ST16)Mission to Gamma VI	$250.00	$500.00
(ST17)Transporter Room (UK only)	$35.00	$200.00
(ST18)Telescreen Console	$75.00	$200.00
(ST19)Tricorder	$75.00	$150.00
(ST20)Super Phaser II	$20.00	$60.00
(ST21)Communicators (boxed)	$75.00	$200.00
(ST22)Communicators (carded)	$75.00	$250.00
(ST23)Communications Console	$35.00	$100.00
(ST24)Tribble	UKN	UKN
(ST25)Trekulator	$75.00	$250.00
(ST26)Planetarium	$300.00	$800.00
(ST27)Periscope	UKN	UKN
(ST28)Sextant	UKN	UKN
(ST29)Battery Operated Radio	UKN	UKN
(ST30)Crystal Radio	UKN	UKN
(ST31)Pressure Chamber	UKN	UKN
(ST32)Telescope	UKN	UKN
(ST33)Electro Magnetic Motor	UKN	UKN
(ST34)Planetarium	UKN	UKN
(ST35)Phaser Battle	$150.00	$400.00

Tex Willer
1974

Italian only 8" action figure line based upon the immensely popular *Tex Willer* comic strip.

Collector Notes:
Action figures were advertised along with Action Jackson.
To date no *Tex Willer* playsets or accessories have been discovered.

TW01

TW01-TW04

TW02-TW04

Tex Willer Italian comic book.

Toy Listings:

Name	Mint Value	MIB Value
(TW01)Tex Willer	$95.00	$200.00
(TW02)Kit Carson	$95.00	$200.00
(TW03)Tiger Jack	$95.00	$200.00
(TW04)Kitt Willer	$95.00	$200.00

Three's Company
1978

Mego obtained the rights to produced action figures based upon this popular sitcom of the late 1970s. A lack of response from retailers limited the product line to one offering.

Collector Notes:
12" figures of Jack and Janet were proposed but never produced.

TC01

Toy Listings:

Name	Mint Value	MIB Value
(TC01)Chrissy	$20.00	$75.00

The Waltons
1975-1976

Popular line of 8" action figures based upon the long-running family drama that appealed to both girls and boys.

Collector Notes:
Action figures were first available in two figure packs and then individually.

WA06 and WA02

WA05 and WA01

WA09

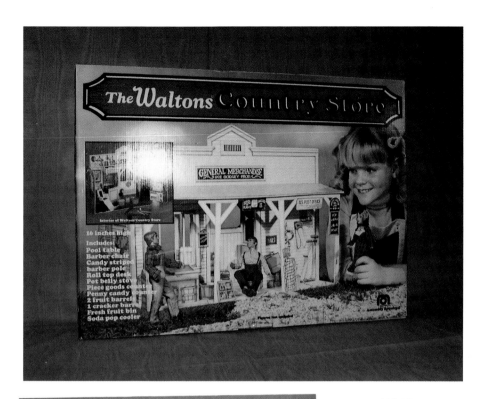

WA10

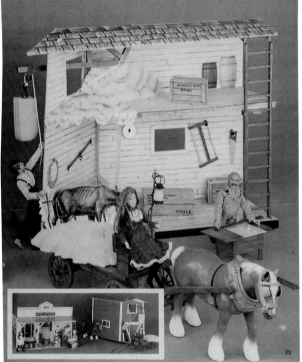

WA11

Toy Listings:

Name	Mint Value	MIB Value
(WA01)John Boy/Ellen	$30.00	$75.00
(WA02)Father/Mother	$30.00	$75.00
(WA03)Grandma/Grandpa	$30.00	$75.00
(WA04)John Boy	$15.00	$75.00
(WA05)Ellen	$15.00	$75.00
(WA06)Father	$15.00	$75.00
(WA04)Mother	$15.00	$75.00
(WA05)Grandma	$15.00	$75.00
(WA06)Grandpa	$15.00	$75.00
(WA07)Farm House	$40.00	$95.00
(WA08)WA08 gift set		NSR
(WA09)Truck	$25.00	$50.00
(WA10)General Store	$50.00	$125.00
(WA11)Barn with Horse	UKN	UKN
(WA12)15" Cloth John Boy	UKN	UKN
(WA13)15" Cloth Ellen	UKN	UKN

Zorro
1977

Mego obtained the rights to produce a *Zorro* action figures when reruns of the 1950s Disney television show became popular in England.

Collector Notes:

Megos 8" Zorro is the only action figure ever licensed and produced based on the famous Disney television show.

ZZ01

ZZ01

Toy Listings:

Name	Mint Value	MIB Value
(ZZ01)Zorro	$300.00	$800.00

Chapter Five
Movie Action Figures

The Black Hole
1980-1981

Mego obtained the master toy license to this high budgeted Disney science fiction film in hoping that it would become a *Star Wars* caliber blockbuster. Unfortunately, the movie opened to lukewarm reviews and quickly faded at the box office.

Collector Notes:
Many *Black Hole* items originally meant for the US were issued in foreign countries.
3 3/4" action figures on US or foreign cards are valued the same.

BH10, BH09, BH08

BH03

BH11 and BH07

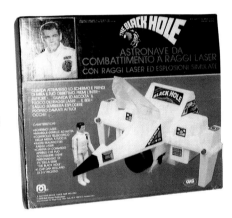

BH13

BH14

BH15

BH25 and BH26

BH25 and BH26

BH21 and BH23

BH24, BH20, BH22

BH16-BH18

BH19

BH31

BH29

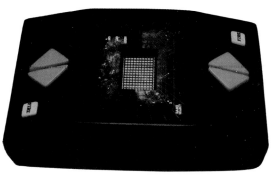

BH30

Toy Listings:

Name	Mint Value	MIB Value
3 3/4" Action Figures:		
(BH01)Dr. Kate McCrae	$10.00	$25.00
(BH02)Dr. Hans Reinhardt	$10.00	$25.00
(BH03)Harry Booth	$10.00	$25.00
(BH04)Capt. Dan Holland	$10.00	$25.00
(BH05)Durant	$10.00	$25.00
(BH06)Pizer	$10.00	$25.00
(BH07)Vincent	$25.00	$75.00
(BH08)Maximilian	$25.00	$75.00
(BH09)Sentry Robot	$25.00	$75.00
(BH10)STAR (Italy)	$150.00	$300.00
(BH11)Old BOB (Italy)	$100.00	$200.00
(BH12)Humanoid (Italy)	$300.00	$600.00
(BH13)Fighter with BHO4 (Italy)	$75.00	$200.00
(BH14)Palomino playset	NP	NP
(BH15)Cygnus Bridge Playset	NP	NP
6" Action Figures:		
(BH16)Magnetic STAR (Italy)	$75.00	$200.00
(BH17)Magnetic V.I.N.cent (Italy)	$75.00	$200.00
(BH18)Magnetic Maximilian (Italy)	$75.00	$200.00
(BH19)Magnetic Old BOB	NP	NP
12" Action Figures:		
(BH20)Dr. Kate McCrae	$20.00	$75.00
(BH21)Dr. Hans Reinhardt	$20.00	$75.00
(BH22)Harry Booth	$25.00	$75.00
(BH23)Capt. Dan Holland	$25.00	$75.00
(BH24)Durant	$25.00	$75.00
(BH25)Pizer	$25.00	$75.00
(BH26)Vincent (Italy)	$300.00	$800.00
(BH27)Remote controlled V.I.N.cent	UKN	UKN
(BH28)Remote controlled Palomino	NP	NP
(BH29)Walkie-Talkies	$75.00	$200.00
(BH30)Video Game	NP	NP
(BH31)Walking Vincent (UK)	$25.00	$60.00

Buck Rogers in the 25th Century
1979-1981

Based upon the movie and TV series of the same name. *Buck Rogers in the 25th Century* was a modest hit for Mego.

Collector Notes:

A 12" Wilma Deering was proposed but never produced.

Licensed 6" action figures were issued in Australia. It is unknown if these were manufactured by Mego.

BR06, BR03, BR08, BR09, BR05

BR02

BR10

BR11

BR12

BR13

BR14

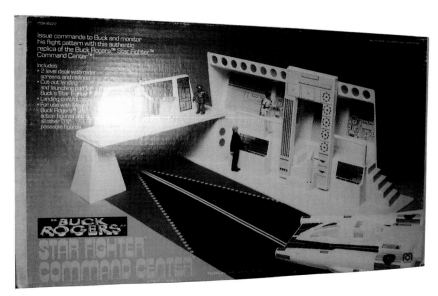

BR15

BR16

BR17 and BR18

BR18

BR21

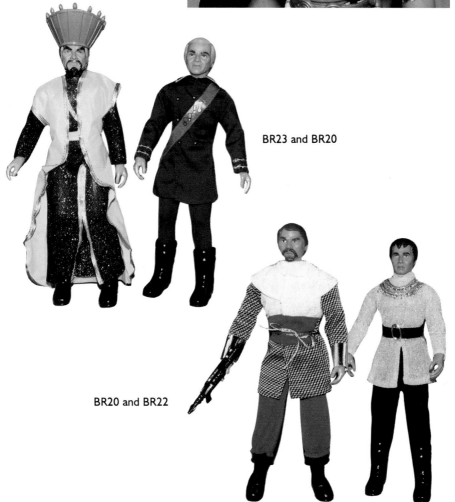

BR23 and BR20

BR20 and BR22

Toy Listings:

Name	Mint Value	MIB Value
3 3/4" Action Figures:		
(BR01)Buck Rogers	$15.00	$40.00
(BR03)Twiki	$15.00	$40.00
(BR05)Killer Kane	$10.00	$25.00
(BR07)Tiger Man	$15.00	$40.00
(BR08)Draconian Guard	$10.00	$25.00
(BR09)Draco	$10.00	$25.00
(BR02)Wilma Deering	$15.00	$40.00
(BR06)Ardella	$10.00	$25.00
(BR04)Dr. Huer	$10.00	$25.00
(BR10)Star Fighter	$30.00	$75.00
(BR11)Draconian Marauder	$20.00	$50.00
(BR12)Laserscope Fighter	$30.00	$75.00
(BR13)Land Rover	$40.00	$100.00
(BR14)Star Searcher	$25.00	$150.00
(BR15)Command Center	$30.00	$75.00
(BR16)6" Figures (Australia) each:	$25.00	$75.00
12" Action Figures:		
(BR17)Buck Rogers	$20.00	$75.00
(BR18)Twiki	$20.00	$75.00
(BR19)Dr. Huer	$20.00	$75.00
(BR20)Killer Kane	$20.00	$75.00
(BR21)Tiger Man	$20.00	$75.00
(BR22)Draconian Guard	$20.00	$75.00
(BR23)Draco	$20.00	$75.00
(BR24)Radio controlled Twiki	N/P	N/P

Grease
1979

Mego unsuccessfully offered retailers a complete line of 8" action figures based on the hit movie.

Collector Notes:

No authentic Grease prototypes have been found by collectors to date.

GR01-GR05

Toy Listings:

Name	Mint Value	MIB Value
(GR01)Danny	NP	NP
(GR02)Sandy	NP	NP
(GR03)Kenickie	NP	NP
(GR04)Rizzo	NP	NP
(GR05)Grease Lighting	NP	NP

King Kong
1977

Die hard *King Kong* fans were not thrilled with this big budgeted remake of the 1933 screen original. Regardless, the movie was a major worldwide hit. *King Kong* was Mego's first venture into the world of movie licensing.

Collector Notes:

Mego issued many King Kong items in Japan which were not available in America. Those that are known to exist are listed.

The Skull Island model kit may have been available in Japan.

KK03

KK06

KK09

KK01 and KK02

KK05

KK01

145

KK08

Toy Listings:

Name	Mint Value	MIB Value
(KK01)6" King Kong (Japan)	$20.00	$75.00
(KK02)6" King Kong with car (Japan)	$20.00	$75.00
(KK03)King Kong playset	$75.00	$200
(KK04)Last Stand Model	$10.00	$35.00
(KK05)Skull Island Model	UKN	UKN
(KK06)Bob Bag	$10.00	$25.00
(KK07)Drinking Straw	$10.00	$25.00
(KK08)Climbing King Kong	UKN	UKN
(KK09)14"" Plush King Kong	$35.00	
(KK10)20" Plush King Kong	UKN	
(KK11)26" Plush King Kong	UKN	

Moonraker
1979

Mego acquired the license to this James Bond film in hopes that it would result in a successful toy line. While the movie was a hit, retailers did not support the line and placed low orders.

Collector Notes:
Because of production delays the 12" Jaws with magnetic teeth was never issued in the US.
A complete line of 3 3/4" figures and accessories was planned but dropped due to a lack of interest by retailers.

JB08

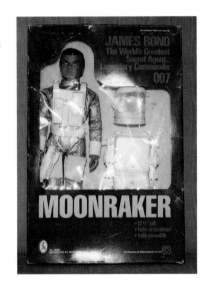

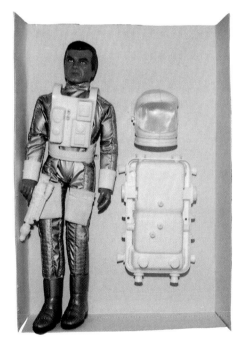

JB08

JB09 and JB07

JB09 and JB10

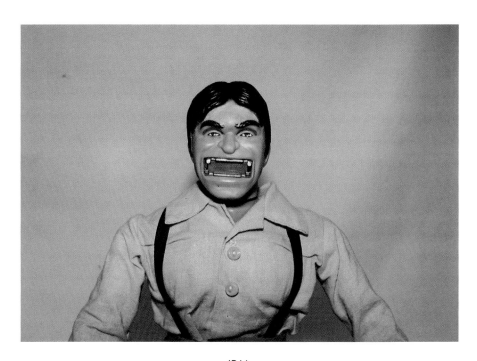

JB11

148

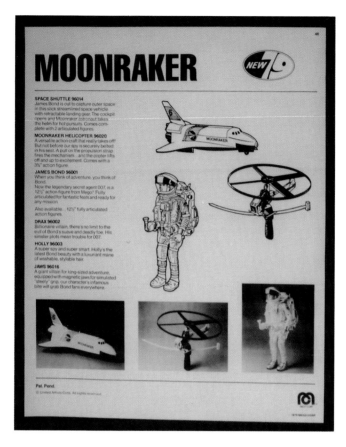

JB05, JB06, JB08

Toy Listings:

Name	Mint Value	MIB Value
3 3/4" Action Figures:		
(JB01)James Bond	NP	NP
(JB02)Holly	NP	NP
(JB03)Drax	NP	NP
(JB04)Jaws	NP	NP
(JB05)Bond with Helicopter	NP	NP
(JB06)Space Shuttle with Astronaut	NP	NP
12" Action Figures:		
(JB07)James Bond	$20.00	$60.00
(JB08)Commander Bond(Italy only)	$100.00	$350.00
(JB09)Holly	$30.00	$100.00
(JB10)Drax	$30.00	$100.00
(JB11)Jaws(Italy only)	$200.00	$450.00

Planet of the Apes
1974-1975

    8" action figures based on the hit science fiction series of *Planet of the Ape* movies. Figures are some of the most popular that Mego ever produced. Release of action figures coincided with both the movie spin off TV series and animated series of the mid 1970s.

Collector Notes:
    Listing includes both movie and TV series characters.

    Montgomery Ward sold the Astronaut as "Taylor" (the character played by Charlton Heston) in its 1974 Christmas mail order catalog.

    The *Action Jackson* Lost Continent playset was also marketed as a Apes playset.

    Mego issued General Urko as Ursus to reflect the name mistake featured in the animated series. The Ursus action figure was also to be issued as Urko.

    Figures were issued in both window box style and blister card. Values for both are listed.

    Figures were available in Japan and Britain. Values for each are given. Figures and accessories from Mexico are NSR as they feature variation outfits and packaging.

PA15 and PA30

PA05 and PA03

PA01 and PA02

PA10 and PA08

PA06 and PA09

PA07 and PA11

PA22

PA44

PA40

PA42 and PA41

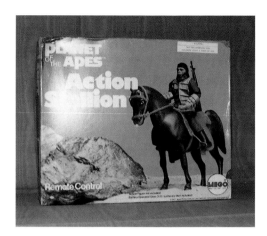

PA38

PA43

PA35

PA36

PA39

PA48

PA37

PA51

PA54, PA52, PA49

Japanese *Planet of the Apes* action figure mini catalog.

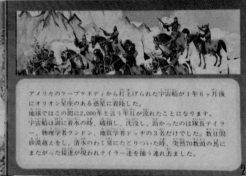

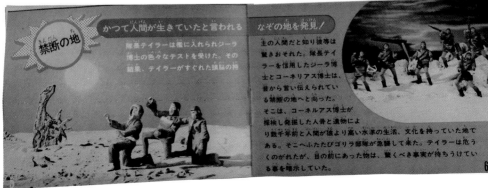

猿の惑星
生活様式
猿人村
ジャングルハウス
7
8

猿人の武器
猿人を無敵にする
強力マシーンシリーズ
〈ゴリラ用〉
アクションホース
ロボットの馬であり、現在の馬の1千頭の馬力を出す。武器をそうてんすると恐ろしい無人ゆうどう弾になる。
レザーガン
一見ふつうの銃の形をしているが、破かい力はウインチェスターの100倍にあたる。
9
10

オランウータンの
開発基地
これが猿人のめざす未来の基地だ！
11
12

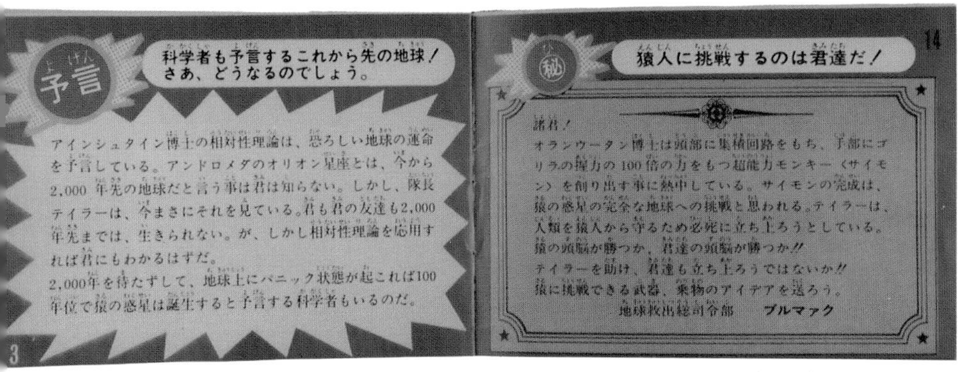
予言

科学者も予言するこれから先の地球！
さあ、どうなるのでしょう。

アインシュタイン博士の相対性理論は、恐ろしい地球の運命を予言している。アンドロメダのオリオン星座とは、今から2,000年先の地球だと言う事は君は知らない。しかし、隊長テイラーは、今まさにそれを見ている。君も君の友達も2,000年先までは、生きられない。が、しかし相対性理論を応用すれば君にもわかるはずだ。
2,000年を待たずして、地球上にパニック状態が起これば100年位で猿の惑星は誕生すると予言する科学者もいるのだ。

13

㊙

猿人に挑戦するのは君達だ！

諸君！
オランウータン博士は頭部に集積回路をもち、手部にゴリラの握力の100倍の力をもつ超能力モンキー〈サイモン〉を創り出す事に熱中している。サイモンの完成は、猿の惑星の完全な地球への挑戦と思われる。テイラーは、人類を猿人から守るため必死に立ち上ろうとしている。
猿の頭脳が勝つか、君達の頭脳が勝つか!!
テイラーを助け、君達も立ち上ろうではないか!!
猿に挑戦できる武器、乗物のアイデアを送ろう。

地球救出総司令部　ブルマァク

14

Toy Listings:

Name	Mint Value	MIB Value
(PA01)Cornelius	$20.00	$75.00
(PA02)Zira	$35.00	$85.00
(PA03)Dr. Zaius	$20.00	$75.00
(PA04)Soldier Ape	$35.00	$85.00
(PA05)Astronaut	$35.00	$85.00
(PA06)General Urko	$60.00	$150.00
(PA07)General Ursus	$60.00	$150.00
(PA08)Peter Burke	$60.00	$150.00
(PA09)Allen Verdon	$60.00	$150.00
(PA10)Galen	$35.00	$85.00
(PA11)General Ursus (Urko)	$60.00	NSR
(PA12)General Urko (Ursus)	$60.00	$175.00
Window Box packaging:		
(PA13)Zira	$35.00	$200.00
(PA14)Dr. Zaius	$20.00	$200.00
(PA15)Astronaut	$35.00	$200.00
(PA16)Soldier Ape	$35.00	$200.00
(PA17)Galen	$50.00	$250.00
(PA18)General Ursus (Urko)	$60.00	NSR
(PA19)General Urko (Ursus)	$60.00	NSR
Bullmark Japan packaging:		
(PA20)Cornelius	$20.00	$200.00
(PA21)Zira	$35.00	$200.00
(PA22)Dr. Zaius	$20.00	$200.00
(PA23)Soldier Ape	$35.00	$200.00
(PA24)Astronaut	$35.00	NSR
Popy UK packaging 1975-1977:		
(PA25)Cornelius	$20.00	NSR
(PA26)Zira	$35.00	$150.00
(PA27)Dr. Zaius	$20.00	$150.00
(PA28)Soldier Ape	$35.00	$150.00
(PA29)Astronaut	$35.00	NSR
(PA30)General Urko	$50.00	$200.00
(PA31)General Ursus	$50.00	$200.00
(PA32)Peter Burke	$50.00	$300.00
(PA33)Allen Verdon	$50.00	$300.00
(PA34)Galen	$35.00	$150.00
(PA35)Village	$50.00	$125.00
(PA36)Tree House	$50.00	$125.00
(PA37)Fortress	$95.00	$250.00
(PA38)Horse	$25.00	$85.00
(PA39)Forbidden Zone	$50.00	$125.00
(PA40)Rock Launcher (UK only)	$25.00	$75.00
(PA41)Throne	$15.00	$45.00
(PA42)Jail	$15.00	$45.00
(PA43)Battering Ram	$15.00	$45.00
(PA44)Catapult and Wagon	$50.00	$125.00
(PA45)PA35 with figures	NA	NSR

(PA46)PA36 with figures	NA	NSR
(PA47)PA37 with figures	NA	NSR
(PA48)Lost Continent	$100.00	$350.00
5" *Bend N' Flex* figures:		
(PA49)Cornelius	$10.00	$45.00
(PA50)Zira	$10.00	$45.00
(PA51)Dr. Zaius	$10.00	$45.00
(PA52)Soldier Ape	$10.00	$45.00
(PA53)Astronaut	$10.00	$45.00
(PA54)Galen	$10.00	$45.00

Star Trek: The Motion Picture
1980-1981

Mego produced a complete line of toys based on the first Star Trek motion picture. While the movie was a hit, the action figures' lack of imaginative bending action led to an poor sales.

Collector Notes:

All of the 3 3/4" Aliens (with the exception of the Klingon, Arcturian, and Rigellian, which were available at JC Penny) were made available in Europe.

A 12" McCoy was designed but never manufactured.

SM23 through SM25 are detailed scaled plastic ships that were issued outside of the US.

SM01. SM04, SM05

SM03, SM06, SM02

SM07, SM12, SM09

SM11, SM10, SM08

SM13

SM14

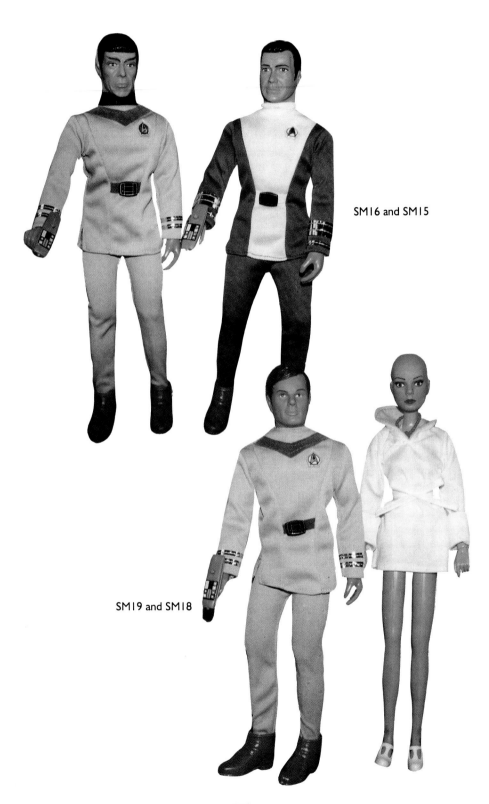

SM16 and SM15

SM19 and SM18

SM21 and SM20

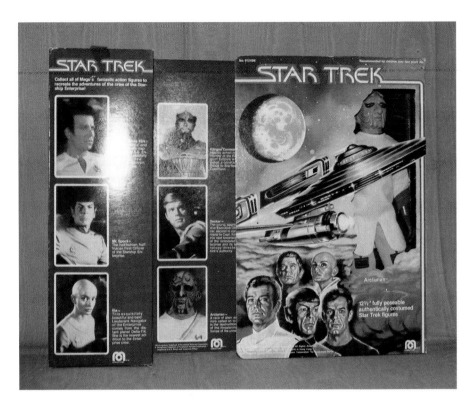

SM21

SM22 and ST21

SM23

SM24 and SM25

Toy Listings:

Name	Mint Value	MIB Value
3 3/4" Action Figures:		
(SM01)Kirk	$5.00	$25.00
(SM02)Spock	$5.00	$25.00
(SM03)McCoy	$5.00	$25.00
(SM04)Scotty	$10.00	$35.00
(SM05)Ilia	$5.00	$25.00
(SM06)Decker	$15.00	$40.00
(SM07)Klingon	$50.00	$125.00
(SM08)Rigellian	$45.00	$125.00
(SM09)Arcturian	$45.00	$125.00
(SM10)Megarite	$45.00	$125.00
(SM11)Zaranite	$45.00	$125.00
(SM12)Betelgeusian	$45.00	$125.00
(SM13)Enterprise Bridge	$75.00	$150.00
(SM14)Vulcan Shuttle	UKN	UKN
12" Action Figures:		
(SM15)Kirk	$25.00	$75.00
(SM16)Spock	$25.00	$75.00
(SM17)Scotty	$25.00	$75.00
(SM18)Ilia	$25.00	$75.00
(SM19)Decker	$65.00	$150.00
(SM20)Klingon	$45.00	$100.00
(SM21)Arcturian	$45.00	$100.00
(SM22)Communicators	$45.00	$100.00
(SM23)Enterprise (foreign)	$125.00	$325.00
(SM24)Klingon Cruiser(foreign)	$100.00	$300.00
(SM25)Vulcan Shuttle(foreign)	$100.00	$300.00

The Wizard of Oz
1975-1976

The Wizard of Oz line of 8" action figures is one of Mego's greatest hits. They are desired and collected by both OZ collectors and action figure enthusiast.

Collector Notes:
Witches Castle was a 1975 Sears Christmas exclusive and only available in a brown packing box.

Mego sold remaining inventory of Dorothy in header card bags.

OZ01 and OZ03

OZ04 and OZ05

OZ02 and OZ08

OZ07 and OZ06

OZ04 and OZ03

OZ10-OZ12

OZ21

OZ07

OZ13

OZ16

OZ15

Accessories from Witches Castle.

OZ17

Z20 and OZI

Toy Listings:

Name	Mint Value	MIB Value
(OZ01)Dorothy	$15.00	$45.00
(OZ02)Lion	$25.00	$65.00
(OZ03)Tin Man	$25.00	$65.00
(OZ04)Scarecrow	$25.00	$65.00
(OZ05)Scarecrow with hair	$25.00	$65.00
(OZ06)Glinda	$35.00	$75.00
(OZ07)Wicked Witch	$35.00	$75.00
(OZ08)Wizard	$25.00	$300.00
(OZ09)Mayor	$40.00	$95.00
(OZ10)Flower Girl	$40.00	$95.00
(OZ11)General	$40.00	$95.00
(OZ12)Dancer	$40.00	$95.00
(OZ13)Emerald City	$40.00	$95.00
(OZ14)Emerald City Gift Set		NSR
(OZ15)Witches Castle with OZ07 (Sears)	$400.00	NA
(OZ16)Munchkin Land with OZ09	$75.00	$200.00
(OZ17)15" Cloth Dorothy	$95.00	$200.00
(OZ18)15" Cloth Lion	$95.00	$200.00
(OZ19)15" Cloth Tin Man	$95.00	$200.00
(OZ20)15" Cloth Scarecrow	$95.00	$200.00
(OZ21)Dorothy in header bag	$15.00	$125.00

Chapter Six
Super Hero Action Figures

Bend 'n Flex Super Heroes
1974-1975

Mego expanded its growing range of Super Hero toys with this line of 5" bendable figures in 1974. Their low cost made them an instant hit with children.

Collector Notes:
> Because of their popularity, carded figures are difficult to find.
> During the late 1980s Batman was reissued in Australia.

BF01, BF03, BF06

BF11, BF12, BF19

BF14, BF05, BF08

BF17

BF01-BF016

Toy Listings:

Name	Mint Value	MIB Value
(BF01)Superman	$15.00	$75.00
(BF02)Batman	$15.00	$75.00
(BF03)Robin	$15.00	$75.00
(BF04)Aquaman	$15.00	$75.00
(BF05)Spiderman	$15.00	$75.00
(BF06)Shazam	$15.00	$75.00
(BF07)Capt. America	$25.00	$100.00
(BF08)Tarzan	$10.00	$50.00
(BF19)Joker	$35.00	$125.00
(BF10)Riddler	$50.00	$150.00
(BF11)Penguin	$35.00	$125.00
(BF12)Mr. Mxyzlptlk	$35.00	$50.00
(BF13)Wonder Woman	$50.00	$175.00
(BF14)Supergirl	$50.00	$175.00
(BF15)Batgirl	$50.00	$175.00
(BF16)Catwoman	$50.00	$175.00
(BF17)Carry Case	UKN	UKN

Comic Action Heroes
1975-1978

3 3/4" *Comic Action Heroes* was Mego's answer for a lower price Super Hero product line. In 1979, the line was updated and renamed *Pocket Super Heroes*.

Collector Notes:
Each figure came with a stand.
Figures were issued in England without stands on single cards or in three-figure packs.
Action figures included with CA16 with the exception of Batman came on display cards.
Both CA22 and CA23 have been found with both *Comic Action* and *Pocket Super Heroes* style figures.

CA13 and CA15

CA01-CA12

CA20

174

CA19

CA17

CA23

CA18

CA22

CA21, CA18, CA22

Toy Listings:

Name	Mint Value	MIB Value
(CA01)Aquaman	$15.00	$65.00
(CA02)Wonder Woman	$15.00	$65.00
(CA03)Shazam	$15.00	$65.00
(CA04)Superman	$15.00	$65.00
(CA05)Batman	$15.00	$65.00
(CA06)Robin	$15.00	$65.00
(CA07)Joker	$15.00	$65.00
(CA08)Penguin	$15.00	$65.00
(CA09)Spiderman	$15.00	$65.00
(CA10)Hulk	$15.00	$65.00
(CA11)Green Goblin	$15.00	$65.00
(CA12)Capt. America	$15.00	$65.00
(CA13)Figure UK each	$15.00	$95.00
(CA14)Three-pack CA04,5,6 (UK)	$45.00	$250.00
(CA15)Three-pack CA02,07,08 (UK)	$45.00	$250.00
(CA16)Bridge with Batmobile and CA05	$75.00	$200.00
(CA17)Bridge with Batmobile and CA05-08	$100.00	$350.00
(CA18)Mangler with CA11	$100.00	$300.00
(CA19)Tower with Invisible Airplane with CA02	$75.00	$150.00
(CA20)Fortress of Solitude with CA04	$100.00	$300.00
(CA21)Exploding Tower includes CA09	NSR	NSR
(CA22)Batcopter with CA05	$75.00	$150.00
(CA23)Spidercar with CA09,11	$50.00	$150.00
(CA24)Batmobile with CA05,06	$50.00	$200.00
(CA25)Comic Action Activator	NA	UKN

DC and Marvel Large Size Super Heroes
1978-1980

For easy reference, we have included all of Mego's 12" DC and Marvel Super Heroes in this section.

Collector Notes:

Values are equal for figures with or without Fly Away action figures.

DC05 and DC06 utilized the Batman and Robin Magnetic bodies without magnetic hands or feet.

LS03, LS04, and LS14 were manufactured specifically for foreign retail sales.

LS03 and LS04

LS01 and LS02

LS11

LS12

178

LS09 and LS14

LS08 and LS07

LS16

Toy Listings:

Name	Mint Value	MIB Value
(LS01)Batman Magnetic	$65.00	$125.00
(LS02)Robin Magnetic	$95.00	$250.00
(LS03)Batman (foreign)	$25.00	$75.00
(LS04)Robin (foreign)	$100.00	$250.00
(LS05)Batman	UKN	UKN
(LS06)Robin	NSR	NSR
(LS07)Spiderman	$15.00	$75.00
(LS08)Spiderman heavy body	$25.00	$95.00
(LS09)Web Spinning Spiderman	$75.00	$200.00
(LS10)Magnetic Spiderman	NP	NP
(LS11)Hulk	$15.00	$75.00
(LS12)Capt. America	$75.00	$200.00
(LS13)Mr. Fantastic	NP	NP
(LS14)Spiderman (foreign)	$15.00	$75.00
(LS15)Dr. Strange	NP	NP
(LS16)22" Growling Hulk	NP	NP

Die Cast Super Heroes
1979-1980

The first truly limited edition action figures aimed specifically at the collectibles market. Each die cast and plastic action figure featured superb styling and detailing.

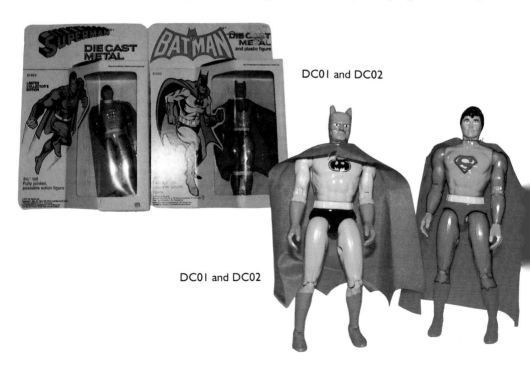

DC01 and DC02

DC01 and DC02

DC04 and DC05

Toy Listings:

Name	Mint Value	MIB Value
(DC01)Batman	$15.00	$65.00
(DC02)Superman	$15.00	$65.00
(DC03)Hulk	$15.00	$65.00
(DC04)Spiderman	$15.00	$65.00

Elastic Super Heroes
(1979-1981)

EH01-EH05

Advertisement for Elastic Spiderman and Hulk.

(EH01)Batman	$25.00	$75.00
(EH02)Superman	$25.00	$75.00
(EH03)Hulk	$25.00	$75.00
(EH04)Spiderman	$25.00	$75.00
(EH05)Plasticman	$75.00	$200.00

Magnetic Super Heroes
1979-1980

Manufactured exclusively for the Italian market, this set of four 8" hard plastic figures are virtually identical to Mego's *Die Cast Super Heroes* except in size.

Collector Notes:
Figures featured magnetic heads, arms, and legs. They were interchangeable with one another so that a child could create a new character.
Figures were first available on blister cards and then in window boxes. Values are the same.

MH03 and MH04

MH01 and MH02

MH04

Toy Listings:

Name	Mint Value	MIB Value
(MH01)Batman	$75.00	$200.00
(MH02)Superman	$75.00	$200.00
(MH03)Spiderman	$75.00	$200.00
(MH04)Hulk	$45.00	$150.00

Pocket Super Heroes
1979-1982

In 1979, Mego updated its popular 3 3/4" *Comic Action Heroes* line into *Pocket Super Heroes*. The figures are basically the same, but unlike their solid leg predecessors, they feature jointed legs.

Collector Notes:

Both PH16 and PH17 have been found with either *Comic Action Hero* or *Pocket Hero Super Hero* type figures. Values are the same.

Under its Lion Rock subsidiary Mego issued a line of shuttle vehicles in England. Action figures have been found in UK and Italian packaging. Values are NSR.

PH16 and PH17

PH01-PH03

PH04-PH06

PH09-PH11

PH12, PH07, PH27

185

PH08 and PH28

PH20-PH24

PH15

186

PH19

PH18

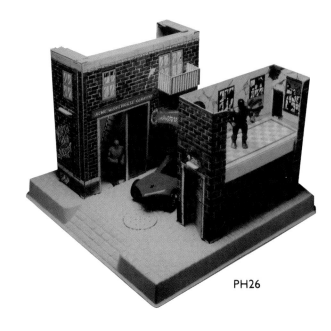

PH26

187

PH27 and PH28

Toy Listings:

Name	Mint Value	MIB Value
(PH01)Batman	$15.00	$50.00
(PH02)Robin	$15.00	$50.00
(PH03)Superman	$15.00	$50.00
(PH04)Lex Luthor	$5.00	$15.00
(PH05)Jorel	$5.00	$15.00
(PH06)Zod	$5.00	$15.00
(PH07)Spiderman	$15.00	$50.00
(PH08)Hulk	$15.00	$50.00
(PH09)Green Goblin	$25.00	$125.00
(PH10)Wonder Woman	$25.00	$125.00
(PH11)Aquaman	$25.00	$125.00
(PH12)Capt. America	$25.00	$125.00
(PH13)Shazam	NP	NP
(PH14)Joker	NP	NP
(PH14)Penguin	NP	NP
(PH15)Batcave	$75.00	$200.00
(PH16)Batmobile with PH01,02	$50.00	$125.00
(PH17)Spidercar with PH09,10	$25.00	$80.00
(PH18)Spidermachine	$25.00	$75.00
(PH19)Batmachine	$30.00	$85.00
(PH20)Hulk Shuttle (UK only)	$10.00	$50.00
(PH21)Spiderman Shuttle (UK only)	$10.00	$50.00
(PH22)Batman Shuttle (UK only)	$15.00	$60.00
(PH23)Robin Shuttle (UK only)	$15.00	$60.00
(PH24)Marvel Shuttle	$15.00	$60.00
(PH25)DC Shuttle	NSR	NSR
(PH26)Spiderman Alley	NP	NP
(PH27)Ampzilla with PH04	NP	NP
(PH28)The Claw with PH09	NP	NP
(PH27)Superman (UK card)	NSR	NSR
(PH28)Hulk (Italian card)	NSR	NSR

188

Superman
1978-1981

In 1978, *Superman The Movie* became a popular hit. Mego quickly produced a line of 12" action figures of each major character. For financial reasons, Mego licensed the comic book characters rather than those actually represented in the movie.

Characters featured the likeness of their movie counterparts but were dressed in their comic book based outfits.

Due to licensing limitations, 12" action figures of the Phantom Zone villains Non and Ursa were not offered.

SM06 was manufactured specifically for foreign retail sales. During the 1980s, a large quantity of these figures was discovered in Canada.

SM06

SM07

SM05 and SM03

SM02 and SM04

German advertisement for Superman figures.

SM09-SM11

SM08

Toy Listings:

Name	Mint Value	MIB Value
(SM01)Superman	$30.00	$95.00
(SM02)Superman with Fly Away Action	$30.00	$95.00
(SM03)Lex Luthor	$30.00	$95.00
(SM04)Jorel	$30.00	$95.00
(SM05)Zod	$30.00	$95.00
(SM06)Superman (Foreign)	$20.00	$75.00
(SM07)Power Action Superman (UK Only)	$100.00	$300.00
(SM08)Superman playset	NP	NP
(SM09)Fortress of Solitude playset	NP	NP
(SM10)Superman Bank	NP	NP
(SM11)Earthquake playset	NP	NP

Super Softies
1974

Mego's attempt at diversifying its popular Super Hero lineup into different segments of the toy market.

Collector Notes:
Regular figures were 18" in height and talking figures 22".

SS06 and SS07

SS01 and SS04

Toy Listings:

Name	Mint Value	MIB Value
(SS01)Batman	$50.00	$125.00
(SS02)Superman	$50.00	$125.00
(SS03)Lone Ranger	$50.00	$125.00
(SS04)Spiderman	$50.00	$125.00
(SS05)Talking Batman	$75.00	$125.00
(SS06)Talking Superman	$75.00	$150.00
(SS07)Talking Lone Ranger	$75.00	$150.00
(SS08)Talking Spiderman	$75.00	$150.00

World's Greatest Super Heroes
1972-1982

Mego's greatest and most endearing action figure line was available across the world. A total of thirty-seven characters were produced over a ten year period.

Collector Notes:

Dare Devil, The Flash, Mr. Freeze, Dr. Strange, Bruce Banner, Sub Mariner, Green Lantern, Dr. Doom, Dr. Octopus, and Sgt. Rock were all designed but failed to be made into action figures.

Mego updated its figures continuously, resulting in countless box, card, figure, and costume variations. Only major variations are listed.

Secret Identity characters were shipped in plain brown boxes. None of the figures have DC or Marvel copyright information on them. Peter Parker utilized the Shazam head but with blue eyes and brown hair.

Foreign issue packaging that is drastically different than US packaging are listed.

Items issued by Empire and Tara Toys were not sanctioned by Mego.

WG35 are *Action Jackson* outfits sold as Super Hero outfits.

DC Heroes and Villains

DC and Marvel Heroes. Isis was licensed from Filmation.

Marvel Heroes

WG60-WG63

WG29 and WG03

WG09 and WG14

WG54, WG31, WG30

WC27 and WC38

WC40 and WG41

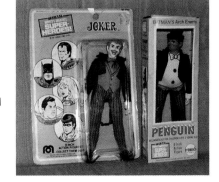

WG57, WG35, WG56, WG55

WG42 and WG43

WC28 and WC59

WC50 and WC45

WC34 and FH97

WM67 and WM64

WM65 and WM66

WG15 and WG18

WG25

FH80 and FH79

FH81 and FH82

FH88 and FH87

201

FH75 and FH7

FH84 and FH77

FH94 and FH33

202

FH93 and FH97

FH89 and FH91

WP03 and WP05

WP24

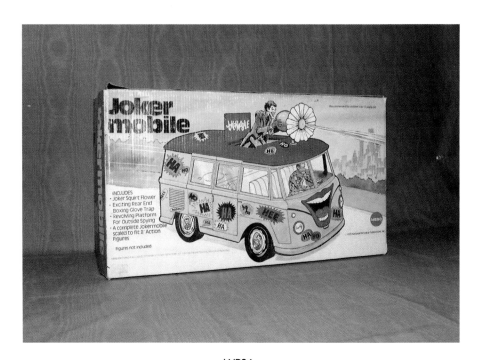

WP26

WP16

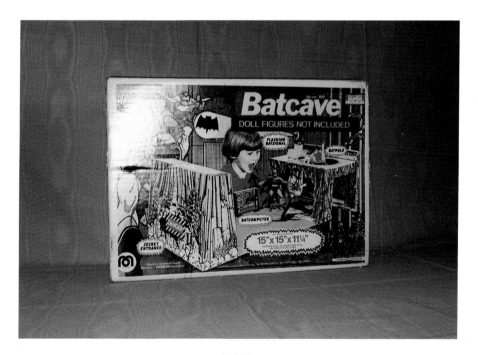

WP18

WP22

WP06 and WP09

WP15 and WP14

WP13

WP11

WP28

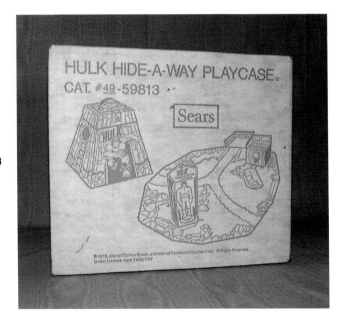

WP23

WP21

WP20

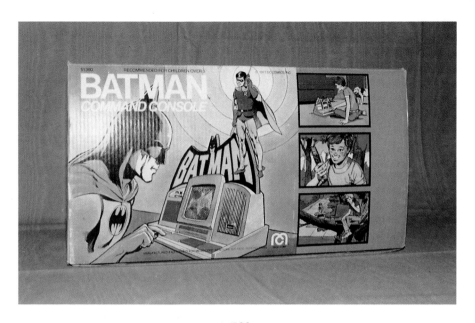

WP39

WP40-WP44

WP37

WP01 and WP02

WP35

WP35

WP45

WP45

Toy Listings:

Name	Mint Value	MIB Value
Solid Box Style package (1972)		
(WG01)Batman with removable cowl	$150.00	$800.00
(WG02)Robin with removable mask	$800.00	NSR
(WG03)Superman	$50.00	$600.00
(WG04)Aquaman	$50.00	$600.00
Kresge Blister Card Style package (1972-74)		
(WG05)Batman with removable cowl	$150	$600.00
(WG06)Batman with painted cowl	$50.00	$350.00
(WG07)Robin with removable mask	$800.00	NSR
(WG08)Robin with painted mask	$50.00	$350.00
(WG09)Superman	$50.00	$350.00
(WG10)Aquaman	$50.00	$350.00
(WG11)Spiderman	$20.00	$350,00
(WH12)Spiderman with circle on chest	$100.00	NSR
(WG13)Capt. America	$50.00	$350.00
(WG14)Tarzan	$50.00	$350.00
(WG15)Wonder Woman	$125.00	$600.00
(WG16)Super Girl	$125.00	$600.00
(WG17)Batgirl	$75.00	$450.00
(WG18)Catwoman	$75.00	$450.00
(WG19)Joker	$65.00	$350.00
(WG20)Penguin	$65.00	$350.00
(WG21)Mr. Mxyzptlk open mouth	$50.00	$450.00
(WG22)Mr.Mxyptlk smirking mouth	$50.00	$450.00
(WG23)Riddler	$75.00	$500.00
(WG24)Shazam	$50.00	$400.00
(WG25)Green Arrow	$100.00	$500.00
Window Box Style package (1973-1976)		
(WG26)Batman with removable cowl	$150.00	$500.00
(WG27)Batman with painted cowl	$50.00	$175.00
(WG28)Robin	$50.00	$175.00
(WG29)Superman	$50.00	$175.00
(WG30)Aquaman	$50.00	$175.00
(WG31)Spiderman	$20.00	$100.00
(WG33)Spiderman Electric Company Box	$20.00	$450.00
(WG34)Capt. America	$50.00	$175.00
(WG35)Tarzan	$50.00	$175.00
(WG36)Wonder Woman	$125.00	$450.00
(WG37)Super Girl	$125.00	$450.00
(WG38)Batgirl	$75.00	$250.00
(WG39)Catwoman	$75.00	$250.00
(WG40)Joker	$65.00	$200.00
(WG41)Penguin	$65.00	$200.00
(WG42)Mr. Mxyzptlk open mouth	$50.00	$200.00
(WG43)Mr. Mxyzptlk smirking mouth	$50.00	$200.00
(WG44)Riddler	$75.00	$400.00
(WG45)Isis	$100.00	$250.00
(WG46)Shazam	$50.00	$175.00

(WG47)Green Arrow	$100.00	$400.00
(WG48)Mr. Fantastic	$25.00	$95.00
(WG49)Invisible Woman	$25.00	$95.00
(WG50)The Thing	$35.00	$95.00
(WG51)Human Torch	$35.00	$95.00
(WG52)Conan	$100.00	$300.00
(WG53)Thor	$100.00	$300.00
(WG54)Hulk	$20.00	$75.00
(WG55)Falcon	$50.00	$200.00
(WG56)Iron Man	$50.00	$200.00
(WG57)Lizard	$75.00	$200.00
(WG58)Green Goblin	$100.00	$300.00
Blister Card Style package (1975-1982)		
(WC27)Batman	$50.00	$125.00
(WC28)Robin	$50.00	$125.00
(WC29)Superman	$50.00	$125.00
(WC30)Aquaman	$50.00	$125.00
(WC33)Spiderman	$20.00	$75.00
(WC34)Capt. America	$50.00	$200.00
(WC35) Tarzan	$50.00	NSR
(WC37)Super Girl	$125.00	$400.00
(WC38)Batgirl	$75.00	$150.00
(WC39)Catwoman	$75.00	$150.00
(WC40)Joker	$65.00	$150.00
(WC41)Penguin	$65.00	$150.00
(WC42)Mr. Mxyzptlk open mouth	$50.00	$300.00
(WC44)Riddler	$75.00	$300.00
(WC45)Shazam	$50.00	$150.00
(WC47)Green Arrow	$100.00	$400.00
(WC48)Mr. Fantastic	$25.00	NSR
(WC49)Invisible Woman	$25.00	NSR
(WC50)The Thing	$35.00	$300.00
(WC51)Human Torch	$35.00	NSR
(WC52)Conan	$125.00	$350.00
(WC53)Thor	$125.00	$350.00
(WC54)Hulk	$20.00	$75.00
(WC55)Falcon	$50.00	$400.00
(WC56)Iron Man	$50.00	$350.00
(WC57)Lizard	$75.00	$400.00
(WC58)Green Goblin	$75.00	$400.00
(WC59)Isis	$75.00	$150.00
(WC60)Kid Flash	$200.00	$500.00
(WC61)Speedy	$200.00	$500.00
(WC62)Aqualad	$200.00	$500.00
(WC63)Wonder Girl	$200.00	$500.00
Secret Identity Figures Ward's exclusives (1974)		
(WM64)Clark Kent	$1000.00	NA
(WM65)Bruce Wayne	$1000.00	NA
(WM66)Dick Grayson	$1000.00	NA
(WM67)Peter Parker	$1400.00	NA
Fist Fighters Window Box packaging (1975-1976)		

(FF68)Batman	$65.00	$275.00
(FF69)Robin	$65.00	$275.00
(FF70)Riddler	$95.00	$350.00
(FF71)Joker	$65.00	$275.00
Fist Fighters Blister Card packaging UK only (1976-1978)		
(FH72)Batman	$65.00	$500.00
(FH73)Robin	$65.00	$500.00
(FH74)Superman	$75.00	$500.00
(FH75)Spiderman	$75.00	$500.00
(FH76)Lizard	$75.00	$500.00
(FH77)Capt. America	$75.00	$500.00
Palitoy England blister packaging (1976-1979)		
(FH78)Batman	$50.00	$300.00
(FH79)Robin	$50.00	$300.00
(FH80)Superman	$50.00	$300.00
(FH81)Penguin	$65.00	$350.00
(FH82)Joker	$65.00	$300.00
(FH83)Spiderman	$20.00	$300.00
(FH84)Hulk	$20.00	$150.00
(FH85)Lizard	$75.00	NSR
(FH86)Capt. America	$50.00	NSR
(FH87)Thing	$20.00	$400.00
(FH88)Human Torch	$20.00	$400.00
Popy Japan Window Box packaging (1978-1980)		
(FH89)Batman	$50.00	$300.00
(FH90)Superman	$50.00	$300.00
(FH91)Spiderman	$20.00	$300.00
Examples of Foreign Blister packaging:		
(FH92)Human Torch Italy	$20.00	$150.00
(FH93)Invisible Woman Italy	$20.00	$150.00
(FH94)Spiderman Italy	$20.00	$150.00
(FH95)Mr. Fantastic Canada	$20.00	$50.00
(FH96)The Thing Canada	$20.00	$60.00
(FH97)Human Torch Canada	$20.00	$60.00
Playsets and Accessories:		
(WP01)Superman Adventure Set	NP	NP
(WP02)Batman Adventure Set	NP	NP
(WP03)Batmobile (photo box)	$45.00	$350.00
(WP04)Batmobile (card display)	$45.00	$150.00
(WP05)Batmobile (drawing box)	$45.00	$100.00
(WP06)Batcycle Black (photo box)	UKN	UKN
(WP07)Batcycle Black (card display)	$95.00	$300.00
(WP08)Batcycle Blue (card display)	$45.00	NSR
(WP09)Batcycle Blue (drawing box)	$45.00	$150.00
(WP10)Batcopter (photo box)	UKN	UKN
(WP11)Batcopter (card display)	$45.00	$100.00
(WP12)Batcopter (drawing box)	$45.00	$100.00
(WP13)Green Arrow Car	$100.00	$350.00
(WP14)Spider Car	$50.00	$125.00
(WP15)Capt America Car	$75.00	$250.00
(WP16)Batcave large box	$75.00	$275.00

(WP17)Batcave gift set with WG01,2		NSR
(WP18)Batcave small box	$75.00	$350.00
(WP19)Bat Signal	NA	UKN
(WP20)Wayne Foundation	$250.00	$500.00
(WP21)Hall of Justice	$100.00	$250.00
(WP22)Aquaman Vs Great White Shark	$200.00	$500.00
(WP23)Supervator	$25.00	$75.00
(WP24)Mobile Batlab	$75.00	$250.00
(WP25)Mobile Batlab gift set with WG01,2		NSR
(WP26)Joker Mobile	$100	$250.00
(WP27)Carry case	$20.00	NA
(WP28)Tara Hulk playcase (Sears)	$40.00	$100.00
(WP29)Empire Hulk Van	$20.00	$50.00
(WP30)Empire Hulk Helicopter	$25.00	$75.00
(WP31)Empire Spiderman Van	$20.00	$50.00
(WP32)Empire Spider Helicopter	$25.00	$75.00
(WP33)Empire Batman Van	$20.00	$50.00
(WP34)Empire Batman Helicopter	$25.00	$75.00
(WP35)Outfits 6 different each	$8.00	$30.00
(WP37)Batrecorder	UKN	UKN
(WP38)Batcoder	$50.00	$150.00
(WP39)Bat Console	$25.00	$100.00
(WP40)Batman Bank	$60.00	
(WP41)Superman Bank	$60.00	
(WP42)Joker Bank	$95.00	
(WP43)Penguin Bank	$95.00	
(WP44)Spiderman Bank	$60.00	
(WP45)Store Displays each:	NSR	NSR

Wonder Woman
1977-1980

Mego produced this line of 12" action figures based on the hit live action television show which ran on ABC and then CBS from 1976 to 1978.

Collector Notes:
First issue Wonder Woman action figure featured a painted bodice and the package featured an actual photograph of star Lynda Carter. Subsequent issues dropped the photograph and featured a cloth bodice.

WW01 and WW04

WW10 and WW03

WW06 and WW05

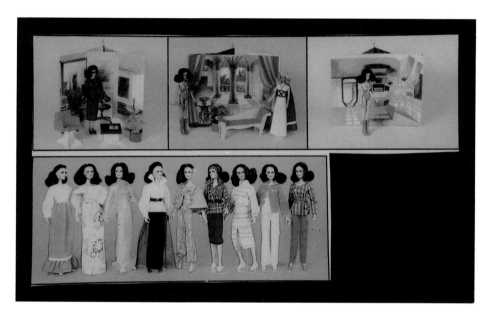

WW08 and WW09

Toy Listings:

Name	Mint Value	MIB Value
(WW01)Figure with Diana Prince outfit	$35.00	$100.00
(WW02)Figure with two fashion outfits	$50.00	$125.00
(WW03)Figure with "Fly Away Action"	$35.00	$100.00
(WW04)Nubia	$35.00	$100.00
(WW05)Queen Hippolyte	$35.00	$100.00
(WW06)Steve Trevor	$35.00	$100.00
(WW07)Paradise Island playset	UKN	UKN
(WW08)Three Way playset	NP	NP
(WW09)Outfits	NP	NP
(WW10)WW01 Canadian package	$35.00	$1000.00

Index